# An Introduction to Low Level Programming for Microprocessors

### J.C. Cluley

*M.Sc., C. Eng., M.I.E.E., F.B.C.S.*

## MACMILLAN
### EDUCATION

First published 1987

Published by
MACMILLAN EDUCATION LTD
Houndmills, Basingstoke, Hampshire RG21 2XS
and London
Companies and representatives
throughout the world

Printed in Hong Kong

British Library Cataloguing in Publication Data
Cluley, J.C.
   An introduction to low level programming for
   microprocessors. — (Macmillan computer science
   series).
   1. Microprocessors — Programming
   I. Title
   005.2'6      QA76.6

ISBN 0-333-43692-X

# Macmillan Computer Science Series

*Consulting Editor*
Professor F.H. Sumner, University of Manchester

S.T. Allworth and R.N. Zobel, *Introduction to Real-time Software Design, second edition*

Ian O. Angell and Gareth Griffith, *High-resolution Computer Graphics Using FORTRAN 77*

Ian O. Angell and Gareth Griffith, *High-resolution Computer Graphics Using Pascal*

M.A. Azmoodeh, *Abstract Data Types and Algorithms*

C. Bamford and P. Curran, *Data Structures, Files and Databases*

Philip Barker, *Author Languages for CAL*

A.N. Barrett and A.L. Mackay, *Spatial Structure and the Microcomputer*

R.E. Berry and B.A.E. Meekings, *A Book on C*

G.M. Birtwistle, *Discrete Event Modelling on Simula*

T.B. Boffey, *Graph Theory in Operations Research*

Richard Bornat, *Understanding and Writing Compilers*

Linda E.M. Brackenbury, *Design of VLSI Systems – A Practical Introduction*

J.K. Buckle, *Software Configuration Management*

W.D. Burnham and A.R. Hall, *Prolog Programming and Applications*

J.C. Cluley, *An Introduction to Low Level Programming for Microprocessors*

J.C. Cluley, *Interfacing to Microprocessors*

Robert Cole, *Computer Communications, second edition*

Derek Coleman, *A Structured Programming Approach to Data*

Andrew J.T. Colin, *Fundamentals of Computer Science*

Andrew J.T. Colin, *Programming and Problem-solving in Algol 68*

S.M. Deen, *Fundamentals of Data Base Systems*

S.M. Deen, *Principles and Practice of Database Systems*

Tim Denvir, *Introduction to Discrete Mathematics for Software Engineering*

P.M. Dew and K.R. James, *Introduction to Numerical Computation in Pascal*

M.R.M. Dunsmuir and G.J. Davies, *Programming the UNIX System*

K.C.E. Gee, *Introduction to Local Area Computer Networks*

J.B. Gosling, *Design of Arithmetic Units for Digital Computers*

Roger Hutty, *Z80 Assembly Language Programming for Students*

Roland N. Ibbett, *The Architecture of High Performance Computers*

Patrick Jaulent, *The 68000 – Hardware and Software*

J.M. King and J.P. Pardoe, *Program Design Using JSP – A Practical Introduction*

H. Kopetz, *Software Reliability*

E.V. Krishnamurthy, *Introductory Theory of Computer Science*

V.P. Lane, *Security of Computer Based Information Systems*

Graham Lee, *From Hardware to Software – an introduction to computers*

A.M. Lister, *Fundamentals of Operating Systems, third edition*

(*continued overleaf*)

# *Contents*

viii                           *Contents*

# *Preface*

This book is intended to provide an introduction to machine code and assembly language programming for students and practising engineers who have some acquaintance with microprocessor architecture and operation.

Although several high level languages are now available for microprocessor systems, there is still a need for those concerned with the design, commissioning and repair of these systems to understand assembly language and machine code. Despite the increased programmer productivity which usually accompanies the change from assembly language to a high level language, the resulting program is often 20 per cent longer than it would be if written in assembly language; it will thus be slower to execute. As a consequence, the time-critical sections of a program are often written in assembly language to obtain the most compact code possible.

Also, when testing microprocessor systems any apparatus which records the sequence of instructions executed, for example a logic state analyser, will sense only binary code. This can be disassembled into assembly language to help the programmer to determine what the system is doing, but there are no facilities for converting the program back into a high level language. The same problem arises when modifying programs which are available only in machine code, for example as loaded into a ROM.

In addition to introducing the principles of writing assembly language programs, this book deals with their subsequent conversion into the machine code which the microprocessor can execute.

The first nine chapters are devoted to basic principles and algorithms, with examples which involve the more widely used 8-bit microprocessors. These are now sufficiently powerful to cope with the majority of industrial tasks, but 16-bit devices are becoming cheaper and are thus being used increasingly in the more demanding applications. In consequence, I have given a brief survey of the main 16-bit microprocessors and a more detailed description of the instruction set and assembly language of one of them — the 68000 — in the last three chapters, including some examples of programming and assembly.

I hope that the book will prove of particular help to students who are beginning a microprocessor project and to practising engineers who are encountering microprocessors systems for the first time.

J.C. Cluley

# 1 Introduction—Microprocessors in the Computing Scene

## 1.1 Microprocessor Systems

In increasing order of power and complexity, computer systems are usually divided into microprocessors, minicomputers, and mainframes. The boundaries between the three categories are, however, rather ill-defined and are continually changing as new products come on to the market. The most important feature of a microprocessor is that it is fabricated on a single slice of silicon, by a process which is highly automated and suitable for high volume production. This is essential for low unit cost, since the initial design, layout and mask making is very expensive. Once this cost has been incurred however, if it can be spread over a million or so chips, the cost of each one may be a few pounds or less.

This technology thus enables one to assemble a small working computer for a cost which is 10 to 100 times smaller than that of a minicomputer of equivalent power. In consequence, most microprocessor applications exploit their characteristics of low cost, small size and low power consumption, often using the microprocessor as the controlling element in some instrument, machine tool, process, or domestic product. In these cases the microprocessor must operate without human intervention, and must start working automatically when power is applied to it.

In contrast, most conventional computers require operators to load programs and data, to attend to peripheral devices such as magnetic tape and disc units, line printers, etc. The difference between these two modes of operation implies certain differences between the design of microprocessor systems and that of larger computers, involving both hardware and programs.

## 1.2 Program Languages and Coding

The only coding for data and programs which computers can directly handle consists of groups of binary digits. The number of digits in the group is an important feature of a computer and corresponds to the size of the data highway which in a microprocessor connects the processor, the store, and the interface packages. In the majority of microprocessors the highway is one byte, or 8 binary digits (bits) wide. For simple applications such as hand calculators 4-bit processors suffice and, where a good deal of accurate computation is needed in a short time, 16-bit processors are now available, with 32-bit systems in development. The greater part of this book is devoted to 8-bit microprocessors.

An 8-bit system can represent positive numbers in the range 0 to 255 decimal, or +127 to −128 if negative numbers need to be encoded. This range is inadequate for precise calculations, and two bytes are often taken together to represent positive numbers from 0 to 65 535, or signed numbers between +32 767 and −32 768. This range suffices for many problems concerned with measurement and control, since it permits much greater precision in representing variables than the vast majority of transducers used to measure pressure, temperature, torque, etc. can attain.

Negative numbers are usually represented in what is called the 2's complement notation. In this, each bit apart from the most significant (left-hand) bit represents a positive number, and the most significant (MS) bit represents a negative number. For an 8-bit system the bit values are shown in the table below.

| Code | Bit Number | | | | | | | | |
|---|---|---|---|---|---|---|---|---|---|
| | 7 | 6 | 5 | 4 | 3 | 2 | 1 | 0 | |
| Unsigned | +128 | +64 | +32 | +16 | +8 | +4 | +2 | +1 | Bit |
| Signed | −128 | +64 | +32 | +16 | +8 | +4 | +2 | +1 | values |

Thus +20 in decimal is represented by 00010100, and −100 by 10011100. In all cases the MS digit is 0 for a positive number and 1 for a negative number, and for this reason is often called the *sign digit*.

Program information, like data, is fed into microprocessors in groups of binary digits. Because instructions vary in their complexity, and thus in the amount of information they need to convey, they vary in size. Thus, for 8-bit systems, instructions may be from one to four bytes long, but always a whole number of bytes.

Although the microprocessor can accept only binary coded information, this representation is extremely awkward for writing down and checking programs. For convenience we need a more compact notation; this is usually obtained by using one symbol to denote four bits so that each byte comprises only two symbols. Consequently each symbol must encompass 16 (or $2^4$) different values. These are obtained by using the 10 numerals and the first 6 letters of the alphabet. We are thus encoding data and instructions in a numbering system with the base 16. This is called *hexadecimal* notation, and is used in all manufacturers' literature to specify instructions and addresses.

Many devices which provide a conventional decimal read out, such as digital voltmeters and frequency meters, provide electrical signals which can be connected to a microprocessor. These usually give a 4-bit version of each decimal digit of the display. Thus a display of 345 would give an electrical output of 0011 0100 0101. This is called *binary coded decimal* (BCD) format and where only simple arithmetic operations on the data are required it may be convenient to keep the data in this form. Many microprocessors have instructions to add BCD numbers, so that simple calculations are possible with some sacrifice in speed. However, this procedure saves the time that would otherwise be devoted to converting from BCD to binary and back to BCD if a decimal output is required. The following table shows the first 20 numbers encoded in different ways.

| Decimal | Binary | Hexadecimal | BCD |
|---------|--------|-------------|-----|
| 0 | 00000 | 00 | 0000 0000 |
| 1 | 00001 | 01 | 0000 0001 |
| 2 | 00010 | 02 | 0000 0010 |
| 3 | 00011 | 03 | 0000 0011 |
| 4 | 00100 | 04 | 0000 0100 |
| 5 | 00101 | 05 | 0000 0101 |
| 6 | 00110 | 06 | 0000 0110 |
| 7 | 00111 | 07 | 0000 0111 |
| 8 | 01000 | 08 | 0000 1000 |
| 9 | 01001 | 09 | 0000 1001 |
| 10 | 01010 | 0A | 0001 0000 |
| 11 | 01011 | 0B | 0001 0001 |
| 12 | 01100 | 0C | 0001 0010 |
| 13 | 01101 | 0D | 0001 0011 |
| 14 | 01110 | 0E | 0001 0100 |
| 15 | 01111 | 0F | 0001 0101 |
| 16 | 10000 | 10 | 0001 0110 |
| 17 | 10001 | 11 | 0001 0111 |
| 18 | 10010 | 12 | 0001 1000 |
| 19 | 10011 | 13 | 0001 1001 |
| 20 | 10100 | 14 | 0010 0000 |

For completeness, the code used to communicate with printers and terminals such as teleprinters and visual display units should be mentioned. This is usually called ASCII (American Standard Code for Information Interchange) although it has now achieved international acceptance as ISO-7 code. This is a 7-bit code which can be sent in either serial or parallel mode. It is often transmitted as an 8-bit byte, where the 8th bit is available for error detection when sending over links such as telephone lines which are liable to noise and interference. A list of ASCII codes is given in appendix 5.

## 1.3    Assembly Languages

Although programs can be written more compactly by using hexadecimal notation rather than binary, a list of instructions such as

$$21$$
$$E0$$
$$0C$$
$$7E$$
$$23$$

does not immediately show what operations are required. In order to help
programmers, manufacturers usually publish a list of mnemonics for the instructions which indicate their function. Typical of these are

| | |
|---|---|
| LDA | Load Accumulator |
| STA | Store Accumulator |
| INC | Increment |
| DEC | Decrement |
| ADD | Add |
| SUB | Subtract |
| ADC | Add with Carry |

With a little practice, this form of coding enables one to read programs as
easily as if they were written in **BASIC**. The instructions listed in hexadecimal
notation at the beginning of the paragraph would be written as

| | |
|---|---|
| LD HL OCEO | Load HL register with OCEO |
| LD A (HL) | Load Accumulator from above address |
| INC HL | Increment Address |

This form of coding is called *Assembly Language* and is clearly easier to read
than the hexadecimal code form, called *Machine Code*. Programs written in
assembly language can be converted into machine code by using programs called
*Assemblers*. More details of these and their use are given in chapter 10.

## 1.4    High Level Languages

Where complex problems are involved it is convenient if the language used to
write the program is designed to suit the problem, rather than arising from the
hardware design of the processor, as assembly language is. A language of this
sort is called a *High Level Language*. It reduces the size of programs drastically,
since each statement, occupying one line, may translate into many machine code

instructions. An assembly language instruction on the other hand normally translates into one machine code instruction. Most microcomputers have facilities for using the language BASIC, which enables a form of algebraic expression to be used. Thus one may specify the value of a variable Z in terms of other quantities X and Y by an expression such as

$$Z = 45.78*SIN(X) + Y\!\uparrow\!4$$

In conventional notation this would be written as

$$Z = 45.78 \sin(X) + Y^4$$

the * denoting multiplication, and the $\uparrow$ exponentiation ($Y\!\uparrow\!4 = Y^4$).

In order to effect this calculation in assembly language one would need to store the coefficients of the power series which evaluates the sin function and include program segments to generate exponential functions. BASIC includes commands to generate square roots, random numbers, logarithms, etc. If these facilities can be used, they avoid the need for much assembly language programming, but the disadvantage is that programs written in BASIC typically take 20 to 30 times longer to run than equivalent programs in assembly language. In some critical control applications, this waste of time cannot be tolerated and assembly language must be used. More often, where the program spends much of its time executing a few subroutines, these can be written in assembly language. The overall program execution time is then much reduced. Many versions of BASIC allow machine code subroutines to be called from programs written in BASIC.

BASIC is slow in execution since it is normally stored in its source form and each statement is converted into machine code immediately before execution, by a program called an *interpreter*. Earlier high level languages such as Fortran which were converted into machine code in a separate operation prior to execution ran at speeds much closer to that of assembly language programs. They were somewhat slower since the machine code produced by the conversion program or compiler was not as compact as that produced by writing directly in assembly language.

BASIC in its original form was inconvenient for many control applications since it made no provision for setting, clearing and testing the individual bits in a byte, tasks often needed in such programs. Later high level languages such as C include this provision and most of them enable machine code program segments to be included in the main high level language program to perform bit handling.

## 1.5   On-line and Off-line Operation

When considering the way in which a microprocessor interacts with its environment and with the devices attached to it, we can distinguish two possible arrangements, called *On-line* and *Off-line*. In the off-line mode the microprocessor is performing some task such as preparing a payroll or calculating the stresses in a structure. Once the program and data have been loaded, the program execution proceeds without further intervention until the results are printed out. There is no direct relation between the time taken for the calculation and any time factors in the problem. In the payroll example, the interval between runs is clearly an upper limit to the running time of an acceptable program, so that a program which took a week to run would not be much use! However, it would not affect the program's utility much if the inclusion of extra features increased the running time from, say, 20 minutes to 25 minutes.

With on-line working the microprocessor is part of a larger system and provides the data handling and computation needed to ensure satisfactory operation. The microprocessor is continuously receiving information from the system and is required to provide outputs which may, for example, regulate the system according to some criterion laid down by the designer. In such an arrangement the microprocessor is required to execute a control program each time a new set of inputs appears, and so to determine what outputs to the system are needed. The running time of the program must be small, otherwise the regulating signals will be fed in too late and the system will become unstable. The control program must contain a segment which scans all of the inputs at regular intervals so that any input changes are rapidly detected and acted upon.

The time available for the program is thus directly linked to the time factors in the system response, or in simpler terms to the delay between the arrival of a disturbance on one of the system inputs and the resulting change in the system output. This limitation may be of little practical significance in systems such as large boilers where conditions can only change relatively slowly, but it becomes a critical factor in the design of very fast systems such as those used for missile guidance.

Other on-line systems which are not involved in regulation or control may impose less stringent conditions on the program. For example, point-of-sale terminals need only keep pace with the relatively slow rate at which the operator can key in details of the transaction.

## 1.6    Dedicated Microprocessor Systems

Most on-line microprocessors form part of a larger system for which they provide the computing and control function. In consequence, they are required to execute only the program needed for this function, and to do so automatically without any human intervention. For example, the microprocessor which is built into a washing machine must begin its control program as soon as the power supply is switched on. This requirement imposes some constraints on the hardware and technology of the microprocessor system and to a lesser extent on the program it executes. The major feature is that the program must be held in the system in an incorruptible form which cannot be overwritten by some unexpected input signal. Also the program must be available the moment power is supplied to the system.

These demands are satisfied by using *Read Only Memory* (ROM) to store the program. The program is either built into the store chip during its fabrication, or loaded in by the system manufacturer, and once the chip is connected into the microprocessor unit its contents cannot be changed. The microprocessor itself has an input labelled RESET or RESTART which must be energised for a few milliseconds after power has been applied to the system. This sets a fixed address into the program counter (a register which holds the address of the next instruction to be executed) and the microprocessor either starts to execute a program beginning at this address, or it reads the contents of this address and the next byte and uses them as a 16-bit address where it will find the starting address of the program. In either case the fixed address which is determined by the manufacturer of the microprocessor must refer to some location in a ROM package. Since this package normally also holds the program, it is convenient to locate the program ROM in the same store area as that chosen for the fixed address. There is no uniformity about this; for example, the 8085 microprocessor always clears the program counter on receipt of a Reset signal, so that the program must always start from location 0000. On the other hand the 6800 always reads the contents of locations FFFE and FFFF to look up the starting address of the program. In this case it is convenient to locate the program ROM at the top of the address space since there must be ROM for the microprocessor to read at all locations from FFF8 to FFFF.

For fully automatic operation, it is essential that the RESET pulse should be generated immediately the power is applied. This can easily be arranged by using a trigger circuit initiated by the rise in voltage of the power supply line; in some microprocessors the trigger circuit may be on the microprocessor chip itself, and the only external components needed are a resistor and a capacitor. The RESET pulse is often extended to the peripheral packages of the system so that registers in these packages can be cleared when power is applied. This ensures that all of these registers will be in a known state when program execution starts.

Some microprocessor systems used in commerce and industry could be described as partly dedicated. They contain a program in ROM variously called a *Monitor, Executive* or *Operating System* which allows the operator to load the program and data for some particular task such as payroll, and then run the program. When this has finished, the next program and its data may be loaded, for example to print invoices. The program and data are normally held on floppy discs which the operator must select and then load into the disc drive. In this kind of system there must be sufficient writable store to hold the various programs one at a time, together with their data. Some microprocessors which are concerned with only a few programs may avoid the need for program storage on disc by holding the program in ROM. If there are several ROMs they can all occupy the same address space and be selected individually when required via the operating system. With this arrangement the system needs only sufficient *Random Address Memory* (RAM) or writable store to hold the data and the complement of ROM and RAM is much nearer to that of a fully dedicated microprocessor.

## 1.7    The Elements of a Microprocessor System

A block diagram of a typical microprocessor system is shown in figure 1.1. The microprocessor chip itself requires a number of other packages to be added to it before it can perform any useful work. In the system shown the processor has a start-up circuit attached which provides the RESET pulse needed to start the program execution. The clock pulse generator provides a regular train of pulses which synchronise the actions of the various packages connected together. Both of these items are entirely hardware-controlled and not affected by the program. This is stored in the ROM package which is connected in a party-line manner to the microprocessor, the RAM and the input/output packages by means of a *Bus* or highway.

The Bus may contain 8 data lines, 16 address lines, and some 8 to 12 lines carrying control and timing information. The programmer has access to *Registers* which can store one or more bytes and form part of the store and input/output packages. The function of the registers in typical microprocessors and associated packages is discussed in more detail in chapter 2.

Data transfers from the microprocessor to the other packages can be used either to store data in the RAM, send a command signal to control a peripheral device, or send data to it. In the other direction, they can be used to read from the stores, examine the state of peripheral devices, or read data from them.

The diagram is simplified in that more than one package of ROM, RAM or input/output may be needed to satisfy the system requirements. Store packages are typically made in a range of sizes, accommodating for example 1K, 2K, 4K, 8K and 16K bytes. By using a suitable combination of these a program of any size can be stored with little unused space.

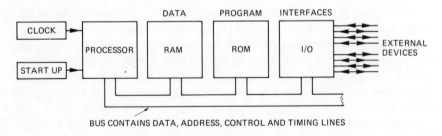

Figure 1.1  Block diagram of typical microprocessor system.

Although few details of the circuit are of direct concern to the programmer, he must know exactly what is connected to each of the input and output lines and what function they perform. Information is exchanged between the microprocessor and the other packages of the system in units of one byte although only one bit may need to be changed to exercise some particular action. Thus the programmer must have instructions available to test, set and clear individual bits of a data byte. Some microprocessors which are intended specifically for control applications have instructions to perform these actions directly; others require several instructions for the same action.

## 1.8   The Need for Development Systems

Although the diagram shown in section 1.7 is typical of many working systems, it is not suitable for developing and testing programs prior to committing them to ROM. A high volume product will normally use a *masked* ROM in which the program is built into the chip in the final metallising process. This connects up all of the cells in the store and determines whether their output is 1 or 0, and requires a special mask containing the program information. The cost of a mask is typically several thousand pounds, so that it is important to ensure that the program contains no faults before ordering the mask. As originally written it is almost certain that there will be some errors, so that an essential feature of a system which is used for development is the ability to load programs, run them, and quickly correct any errors found. The program is held in RAM and when it appears correct a copy must be taken to make the mask, or to load a programmable ROM (PROM).

A range of systems has been offered for development, ranging from simple arrangements which provide a hexadecimal keyboard for data input and a set of 7 segment lamps for the display to more complex systems which include an assembler, a printer or VDU for the display, and provision for automatically loading the program into a PROM. Such systems often include a floppy disc store for programs under development and perhaps a serial data channel to feed in programs which have been assembled in a larger computer, or to 'down-load' an assembled program into a microprocessor in order to test it.

In order to test the program and locate faults in it, a monitor program is generally used. This will allow user programs to be run an instruction at a time, with provision for examining the processor registers after each step, or running the program at full speed until a 'breakpoint' is reached and then single stepping. It will also enable any program instruction to be changed when a fault is found. More detailed consideration of the use of these facilities is given in chapter 10.

# 2 Microprocessor Registers and their Functions

## 2.1 The Accumulator

Most of the program activity in microprocessor systems is concerned with moving information into and out of various registers. These are high-speed storage elements inside the central processor. Consequently, before discussing the action of different instructions it is necessary to understand the way in which microprocessor registers are used and their particular functions. Not all microprocessors have the same set of registers, but all of them have one or more *Accumulators*.

The Accumulator is the main register concerned with arithmetic and logical operations because the result of nearly all such actions is loaded into the accumulator. Also input and output transfers normally copy the contents of the accumulator onto the bus and thence into the data register of some peripheral package, or copy the contents of such a register into the accumulator. In the latter case the previous contents of the accumulator would be destroyed.

In 8-bit microprocessors the accumulator is an 8-bit register, but some devices allow two registers to be used together to store a 16-bit number. For example all members of the 6800 family have two accumulators, and almost all instructions involving accumulators have two versions, one using accumulator A and the other accumulator B. One member of the family, the 6809, has a multiply instruction in which the two 8-bit numbers in the two accumulators are multiplied together and the product is left in both accumulators as a 16-bit number, the most significant byte in accumulator A, and the least significant byte in accumulator B.

Associated with the accumulator is the flag register, also called the condition code register or the processor status register. This comprises a number of status bits which are set after arithmetic operations if certain conditions are satisfied and cleared if not. The usual conditions are

1. Zero result
2. Negative result
3. Overflow
4. Carry
5. Half-carry

Overflow denotes a carry from bit 6 to bit 7 of the result, meaning that two positive quantities have been added together to form a sum too large for the accumulator to handle, so that it represents a negative number. Alternatively, two negative numbers have been added to give a positive sum. The carry bit is in effect an extra 9th bit which holds a carry from the 8th bit of the accumulator. It is also used as part of the circulation path in many Rotate instructions. The half-carry bit is set when a carry from bit 3 to bit 4 occurs. This information is needed for performing arithmetic on BCD numbers. Other bits may indicate that the interrupt line is disabled, or may denote the parity of the accumulator contents.

## 2.2 The Program Counter

The Program Counter (PC) is usually a 16-bit register which is used to keep track of the program execution. It always contains the address of the next instruction byte required by the processor, and so its contents are used to fetch each instruction in turn, byte by byte. Its initial contents are either fixed by the manufacturer, or are stored at two addresses fixed by the manufacturer. In the latter case the microprocessor is built so that on receipt of the Reset pulse it uses the contents of these locations as the starting address of the program.

The programmer can change the contents of the PC by means of a branch or jump instruction, or by a return from subroutine or return from interrupt, but not by direct arithmetic operations. When jumping to a subroutine, the contents of the PC (the return link) must be saved and then restored at the end of the subroutine, to allow the processor to continue execution of the main program. The two actions are carried out automatically as part of the Jump to Subroutine and the Return from Subroutine instructions, and require no further action by the programmer.

## 2.3 Stack Pointer

The stack pointer is another 16-bit register used to control access to the *Stack*. This is an area of RAM which is used to store the return link for subroutines and interrupt service programs, and may also be used by the programmer to store variables temporarily, or to transfer them between the main program and a subroutine. The stack is organised in a different way from normal RAM in that no addresses are specified when putting a byte into store or removing it from store. The only access is to the top location of the stack; as this fills up the address of the next free location is held by a 16-bit register called the *Stack Pointer*. By convention the stack starts at the highest address of the block of RAM allocated to it. Each time an item is loaded onto the stack the stack pointer is afterwards decremented (1 is subtracted from it). Conversely, each time an item is removed from the stack, the stack pointer is incremented (1 is added to it) before using it to point to the item.

Figure 2.1 shows the changes to the stack as two items are added to it and one is removed. The stack is initially empty and its top address is 500 (hex). The operation of putting an item onto the stack is called *Push* and that of removing it is called *Pull* or *Pop*. This type of store is also called LIFO (Last In First Out), and it is very convenient for storing subroutine return links. If subroutines are *Nested*, that is one subroutine can call another subroutine, the return links are automatically put onto the stack so that they are in the correct order to pull from the stack when returning to the main program.

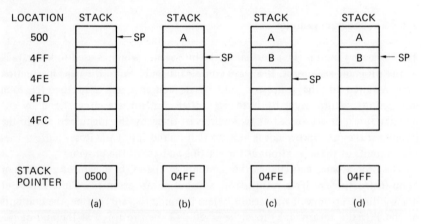

Figure 2.1  Contents of stack and stack pointer as stack is used:
(a) empty; (b) byte A loaded; (c) byte B loaded; (d) byte B pulled off stack.

Only a limited number of operations can normally be performed on the contents of the stack pointer such as loading or storing, and incrementing or decrementing. Some microprocessors, however, allow them to be used in 16-bit addition and subtraction. In all cases the stack pointer must be initially loaded with the address of the top of the stack before any stack operations can be performed satisfactorily.

## 2.4   The Index Register

The index register (IR) is a 16-bit register which is intended to help addressing sequentially the items in a block of data. For example, if we require to add together all of the items, we can use the same add instruction repeatedly by means of indexed addressing. The format of the instruction is

ADD X,20

This means 'Add to accumulator using indexed addressing with an offset of 20'. The address of the item added is obtained by adding together the contents of the IR and the offset 20 (normally taken as hexadecimal). The same instruction will handle the next item in the list if the contents of the IR are first incremented. The program uses a small loop for this action and has the advantage that its size is the same however many items there are in the list. Examples of the use of the IR for this purpose are given in chapter 7.

The index register may also be used for looking up a particular item in a table. For example, if we require the 6th item we can load the address of the first item into the IR. We can then either add 6 to the IR or increment it 6 times. Most microprocessors provide instructions for incrementing and decrementing the IR, but its contents need to be moved to the store or to another register pair in order to add to them.

Where a block of data needs moving from one store area to another a single IR is awkward to use, and the program can be shorter and run more quickly if two IRs are available. One can index the addresses of the originating block, and the other the addresses of the block into which the data is moved. For this reason some microprocessors are provided with two IRs.

The IR is also used as a 16-bit register for counting or timing where indexed addressing is not needed.

## 2.5   Auxiliary Registers

Some microprocessors, for example the Z80, 8080 and 8085, which have a single accumulator include a number of general-purpose registers which can be used to hold data being used in a calculation. Their contents can be incremented, decremented, added to, or subtracted from the contents of the accumulator. Data held in them need not be moved into the store and returned when needed, so saving time in running the program. Pairs of them can also be used to hold 16-bit numbers or 16-bit addresses.

The Z80 has some registers duplicated to allow rapid response to a program interrupt. The instructions for using these and their advantages are discussed in chapter 8.

## 2.6   6800 Microprocessor Architecture

Having explained the function of the various processor registers in general terms, we now turn to the architecture of typical microprocessors as they concern the programmer, starting with the 6800. This was designed by Motorola, but has since been second sourced by a number of other manufacturers. Its instruction set and design bear a marked resemblance to those of the PDP-11 minicomputer, a 16-bit family of minicomputers made by Digital Equipment Corporation. The register set is shown in figure 2.2. Its particular feature is that two accumulators are provided, so simplifying many arithmetic operations. Almost all instructions have two versions, one using accumulator A and the other accumulator B. The only exceptions are DAA which adjusts an Add operation to cope with BCD data and is available only with accumulator A, and ABA which adds together the contents of the two accumulators, but leaves the result in accumulator A.

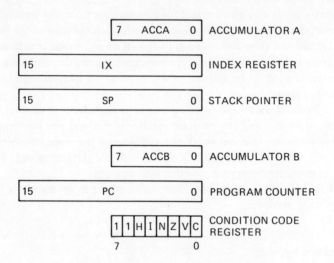

Figure 2.2  6800 microprocessor registers.

There are no auxiliary 8-bit registers, but the IR can be used as a counter or register if not needed for indexed addressing. Like the PDP-11, the 6800 is a universal bus device in which all types of storage package and all input/output registers share a common address space of 64K bytes, using 16 address lines. This has the advantage that the full set of arithmetic and logical instructions can be performed on the registers of the input/output packages. Earlier microprocessors, such as the 8080, had only two input/output instructions; one copied the contents of the accumulator out to the input/output package, and the other sent data in the reverse direction.

The flags are collected in the condition code register and their significance is shown in the table below. The two most significant bits are not connected and so always read as 1.

| Bit Number | Condition |
|:---:|:---|
| 0 | Carry |
| 1 | Overflow |
| 2 | Zero |
| 3 | Negative |
| 4 | Interrupt |
| 5 | Half-Carry |

## 2.7 Z80 Instruction Set

The Z80 was designed by Zilog Inc. to be upwards compatible with the 8080, so that its register set resembles that of the earlier machine. Extra registers are also included to provide quicker block moving operations, more comprehensive interrupt handling, and simple refreshing of dynamic RAMs. It is now made by several other manufacturers.

Only one accumulator (A) is included but four general-purpose single byte registers — B, C, D, and E — allow a number of variables to be held in the processor. This saves time when they are required for computation since they can be loaded into the accumulator in four clock cycles compared with the seven cycles needed to fetch data from the external store. Two other registers (H and L) hold the address of the location in the store which is to be accessed, and if not needed for this can be used as general-purpose registers. The complete set is shown in figure 2.3.

In order to speed up the handling of interrupts, duplicate registers A' to L' are provided so that the state of the processor need not be saved in external storage during the interrupt handling routine.

Pairs of registers (BC, DE, and HL) can be used together to hold 16-bit numbers, with limited facilities for arithmetic operations.

Block data move operations are aided by having two index registers, one of which can be used to select the source and the other the destination of the move. The I register can be loaded by program and holds the most significant byte of the vector address when Interrupt mode 2 is enabled. For completeness the Refresh register is shown, although this cannot be accessed by the programmer. It is used to generate a refresh address for dynamic RAM which is output on the address lines when these are not otherwise needed by the processor. Its contents are incremented after each transfer by the processor and no program action is needed.

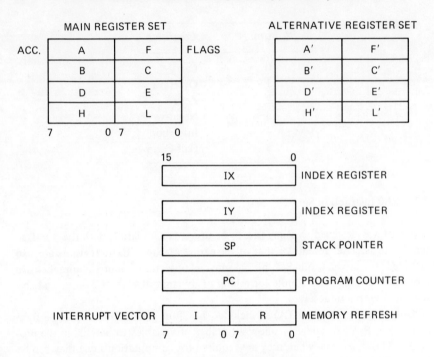

Figure 2.3  Z80 microprocessor registers.

The accumulator flags are collected in a Flag register and are located as follows.

| Bit Number | Condition |
|:---:|:---|
| 0 | Carry |
| 1 | Subtract |
| 2 | Parity/Overflow |
| 4 | Half-Carry |
| 6 | Zero |
| 7 | Sign |

The flag meanings are slightly different from those of the 6800. Bit 1 is set if the last operation was a subtract, otherwise it is cleared. Bit 2 has two functions; it is set if the result of the last arithmetic operation was an overflow, otherwise it indicates even parity of a logical operation. It is thus set for even parity (an even number of ones in the byte), and cleared for odd parity.

The program counter and the stack pointer operate in exactly the same way as the corresponding registers in the 6800.

## 2.8   6502 Register Set

The 6502 was designed by Rockwell International Corp. and bears a family resemblance to the 6800. It is now made by several other manufacturers. It has only one accumulator, however, and two index registers, but these store only 8 bits. The program counter stores 16 bits, as usual, but the stack pointer holds only one byte. It has a 9th bit hardwired as a 1 so that it can store addresses in the range 100 to 1FF (hex). Figure 2.4 shows the set of 6502 registers.

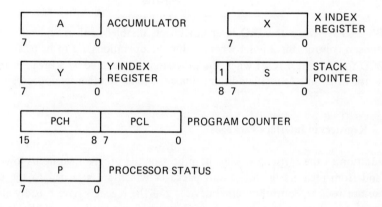

Figure 2.4  6502 microprocessor registers.

Although there are two index registers each one holds only 8 bits, thus restricting the IR. However, any store location can be accessed because the instruction for indexed addressing contains three bytes. The first is the operation code, and the second and third contain a 16-bit address which is added to the IR to obtain the effective address. This is different from the scheme used in other chips in which the IR holds 16 bits and the displacement coded in the instruction holds only 8 bits. The two IRs (X and Y) can also be used for indirect addressing; that means that the effective address calculated from the instruction and the IR contains not the operand but the address of the operand. The 6502 has thus a greater variety of addressing modes than the two previous microprocessors. These are discussed in greater detail in the next chapter.

The flags are collected in a processor status register and have the significance as shown in the table below.

| Bit Number | Condition |
|:---:|:---|
| 0 | Carry |
| 1 | Zero |
| 2 | Interrupt Disable |
| 3 | Decimal Mode |
| 4 | Break Bit |
| 6 | Overflow |
| 7 | Negative |

Bit 2 is set when the IRQ interrupt line is disabled, and is under the programmer's control. Bit 3 is set when arithmetic operations are to be performed in BCD format. Bit 4 is set when the program is interrupted by a Break instruction. The other bits denote conditions similar to those in other microprocessors.


## 2.9    Registers in Interface Packages

In addition to the registers within the processor the programmer needs to write to and from registers in the various packages which are attached to the bus. These are used to control external devices and the registers have broadly three functions: to handle data, to read information about the status of the device, and to write commands to it. In addition the interface package can be configured in a number of ways by program, so that before passing data control registers must be loaded to determine the exact function of the package. For example, in a parallel input/output package we may need to specify

(a)  Whether control signals can create program interrupts.
(b)  Whether each data line is an input or an output.
(c)  Whether the control line sets a flag on the rising edge or the falling edge of its input signal.
(d)  Whether one control line is to be an input or an output.

In some cases only a few control lines are needed and a single-byte register can hold both status (read) and control (write) bits. When performing a read operation to determine, for example, whether a flag is set it will then be necessary to mask out the other status bits and the control bits so that the flag information only is presented. More detailed discussion of the programming of input/output operations is given in chapter 9.

# 3 Instruction Formats and Address Modes

## 3.1 Instruction Formats

All microprocessor instructions comprise a whole number of bytes; the first always contains the operation code (often abbreviated to op. code). If the instruction does not need to specify an operand or its address, this single byte suffices. Some examples are given below in the customary hexadecimal coding.

| Microprocessor | Mnemonic | Code | Action |
|---|---|---|---|
| 6800 | CLRA | 4F | Clear Acc. A |
| 6800 | COMA | 43 | Complement Acc. A |
| 6800 | DECA | 4A | Decrement Acc. A |
| 6800 | INCA | 4C | Increment Acc. A |
| 6800 | INX | 08 | Increment IR |
| | | | |
| Z80 | LD A, B | 78 | Copy B Reg. to Acc. |
| Z80 | LD B, A | 47 | Copy Acc. to B |
| Z80 | INC A | 3C | Increment Acc. |
| Z80 | DEC A | 3D | Decrement Acc. |
| Z80 | ADD A,B | 80 | Add B to Acc. |
| | | | |
| 6502 | TAX | AA | Copy Acc. to X Reg. |
| 6502 | INX | E8 | Increment X Reg. |
| 6502 | DEX | CA | Decrement X Reg. |
| 6502 | ROL A | 2A | Rotate Acc. left |

Two-byte instructions provide one byte for the op. code and one for the address of the operand, or the operand itself. Clearly, with this restriction, only part of the store can be accessed, usually Page 0 (the first 256 bytes), and if the operand is held in the second byte the instruction can load only an 8-bit register. The operand, like the op. code, is normally given in hexadecimal code, but some assemblers allow decimal or binary numbers if these are preceded by a marker symbol.

19

Typical two-byte instructions are

| Microprocessor | Mnemonic | Op. Code | Action |
|---|---|---|---|
| 6800 | ADDA # n | 8B | Add n to Acc. A |
| 6800 | ADDA n | 9B | Add (n) to A |
| 6800 | ANDA # n | 84 | AND A with n |
| 6800 | LDAA # n | 86 | Load n into A |
| 6800 | LDAA n | 96 | Load (n) into A |
| Z80 | LD B, n | 06 | Load n into B |
| Z80 | ADD A, n | C6 | Add n to A |
| Z80 | AND n | E6 | AND A with n |
| Z80 | OR n | F6 | OR A with n |
| 6502 | LDA # n | A9 | Load n into A |
| 6502 | LDA n | A5 | Load (n) into A |
| 6502 | CMP # n | C9 | Compare n with A |
| 6502 | LDX # n | A2 | Load n into Reg. X |

Here, in the right-hand column n denotes an operand, (n) denotes the contents of location n.

The second byte of the instructions for the 6800 and the 6502 can be either the operand or its address. In order to distinguish between these two, a hash sign (#) precedes an operand. Thus

$$LDA \# 10$$

means 'Load the Accumulator with the numerical value 10', whereas

$$LDA \ 10$$

means 'Load the Accumulator with the contents of location 10'. The numbers are normally given in hexadecimal coding. The Z80 has no instructions which embody a single-byte address, so all the examples above refer to the operand itself and there is no need for the hash sign.

Branch instructions are normally two-byte instructions; the second byte contains the offset or displacement. This is the number which must be added to the program counter if the branch condition is satisfied. Since the number is involved in the calculation of the effective address and is not an operand, the hash sign is not needed.

Three-byte instructions normally involve either a full 16-bit address or a 16-bit operand as the last two bytes. They are thus required when loading 16-bit registers or pairs of 8-bit registers, as shown in the examples below.

| Microprocessor | Mnemonic | Code | Action |
|---|---|---|---|
| 6800 | ADDA 2000 | BB2000 | Add to A contents of Location 2000 |
| 6800 | DEC 3000 | 7A3000 | Decrement contents of Location 3000 |
| 6800 | LDX 4000 | CE4000 | Load 4000 into IR |
| Z80 | LD SP, 5000 | 310050 | Load 5000 into SP |
| Z80 | LD HL, 6000 | 210060 | Load 6000 into register pair HL |
| Z80 | LD A, (7000) | 3A0070 | Load contents of Location 7000 into A |
| 6502 | LDA 1000 | AD0010 | Load contents of Location 1000 into A |
| 6502 | LDX 2000 | AE0020 | Load contents of Loc. 2000 into X reg. |

An examination of the instruction codes shows one of the difficulties in machine code programming — the lack of a uniform method of specifying 16-bit numbers. In the 6800 the high-order byte is coded first, whereas in the Z80 and the 6502 the low-order byte comes first. Thus in the 6502 the op. code for Load Accumulator with an immediate operand is AD, and to load the operand 1234 the code required is

AD 34 12

Of the three microprocessors discussed here only the Z80 has four-byte instructions. They are used for the bit test, set and clear instructions where a particular bit of a particular register must be specified, and also the operation to be performed on it. Also operations such as loading an index register use a two-byte op. code. For example, to load index register IX with the operand 1234 would require the four bytes

FD 21 34 12

## 3.2 Addressing Modes

Microprocessor instructions allow either one or two bytes for the address. The number concerned may be interpreted in a variety of ways, called *address modes*, each involving a different method of calculating the Effective Address, or the location which holds the actual operand.

The following list includes those generally found in microprocessor instruction sets.

(a) Immediate Address. In this case the number stored in the instruction is the operand itself, sometimes called a 'Literal'. It consists of one byte for an 8-bit operation, and two bytes for a 16-bit operation.

(b) Direct Address. This means that the one or two bytes after the op. code contain the actual address of the operand. It is also called Absolute Addressing. Some microprocessors have special instructions for accessing the bottom 256 bytes of the store; this needs only one address byte and so the instruction takes up less storage space than one with a 16-bit address and also executes in less time. It, of course, requires that this area of the store should contain RAM used to hold variables and temporary data. In the 6800 this is called Direct Addressing and in the 6502 Page Zero Addressing. It is not provided in the Z80 since the bottom of the store is needed for program.

(c) Indexed Address. This is generally a two-byte instruction in which the second byte holds an offset which is added to the contents of the index register to generate the effective address. The offset is normally treated as an unsigned number. An example in 6800 code is

### LDAA 50, X

This encodes to A6 50. It will load accumulator A with the contents of location 1050 if the IR contains 1000. The IR contents are sometimes called the Base Address. The main purpose of indexed addressing is to allow lists and blocks of data to be handled easily. For example, the same instruction can be used repeatedly to access successive items of data by incrementing the IR before each operation. Some examples of this are given in chapter 7.

(d) Relative Address. In this mode the second byte of the instruction contains a number (often called the *offset*) in two's complement notation which has to be added to the contents of the PC to obtain the effective address. The address is thus computed relative to the PC. A one-byte number limits the offset to between +127 and –128. Note that the offset has to be added after the instruction has been fetched, and is thus added to the address of the first byte of the *following* instruction.

Relative addressing is used mainly for branch instructions; for example, the op. code for 'Branch if not equal to zero' (BNE) is 26. For the program segment shown in figure 3.1 a branch to location 107 needs the PC to be advanced two bytes, so the offset XX must be 02. For a branch backwards to location 101, the PC must be reduced by 4. The offset is thus –04, or in two's complement notation FC. This can be derived by subtracting 4 from

100 in hexadecimal notation, or by converting 04 into binary notation and calculating the two's complement. In either case one can check that the offset is correct by imagining that it is held in the location which the PC points to, here location 105. Counting upwards in hexadecimal towards the destination of the branch should bring the number to 100 on arrival there. Thus we start at 105 containing FC and proceed

$$104 - FD$$
$$103 - FE$$
$$102 - FF$$
$$101 - 100$$

Since the destination is 101 the offset is correct. In this example the BNE instruction is a Conditional Branch, in which the branch occurs only if the result of the previous operation was non-zero; otherwise the next instruction starting in location 105 will be executed.

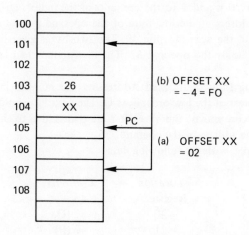

Figure 3.1 Offset calculations for relative addressing.

(e) Indirect Address. In this mode the instruction specifies either a register pair or a store location. The register pair contains the *address* of the operand; the store location and the location above it contains the 16-bit address of the operand. A register pair used in this way is sometimes called a *Data Pointer*. Indirect addressing is available in the Z80 and the 6502 and so the specified address in the store contains the low byte of the operand address, and the next location the high byte. In the 8080 the HL register pair was allocated for indirect addressing and this was the only way of accessing the store. The Z80, however, allows either BC or DE to be used, or two store locations.

The 6502 has only one simple indirectly addressed instruction, an indirect jump. This has a two-byte number following the op. code which gives the address of the first (low-order) byte of the operand address. The high byte is held in the next store byte. The 6502 also allows an index register to be used for Indexed Indirect Addressing, or for Indirect Indexed Addressing. In the first of these the contents of the X register are added to the number given in the instruction. This gives the address of the low-order byte of the operand. For example, if the following were the contents of the registers and locations given

| Location | Contents |
|---|---|
| X Register | 28 |
| 48 | 80 |
| 49 | 31 |
| 3180 | 52 |

the instruction LDA (20, X) would be interpreted as follows.

The offset 20 is added to the contents of the index register X to give 48. This is the address of the low byte of the operand (80), and the high byte (31) is held in the next location 49. The two bytes give the 16-bit address 3180 which holds the operand 52. The instruction then loads 52 into the accumulator.

When using Indirect Indexed Addressing the number in the instruction gives the address of the low-order byte Q. The next byte holds the high-order byte P. The contents of the Y register are then added to the 16-bit number PQ to give the address of the operand.

For example, with the following data

| Location | Contents |
|---|---|
| Register Y | 43 |
| 20 | 32 (Q) |
| 21 | 47 (P) |
| 4775 | 6F |

the instruction LDA (20),Y would be interpreted as follows.

The location 20 gives the address of the low byte Q and the address of the high byte P is 21. Two store read operations give the two bytes P and Q which form the 16-bit address 4732. The contents of the Y register are added to this to give 4775, which contains the operand 6F. The final action is to load 6F into the accumulator.

Both of these forms of indirect and indexed addressing allow two parameters of the address to be changed: the register contents and the location held in the store. There is thus scope for quite complicated list seaching and look-up tables.

(f)  Implicit Addressing. This is the mode where the address is indicated in the op. code. It is sometimes called Implied or Inherent Addressing. An example is CLRA (Clear Accumulator A) in the 6800 which requires the single-byte instruction 4F.

(g)  Bit Addressing. This is available in the Z80 and in some single chip microprocessors. It allows a single bit of a specified register to be set, cleared, or tested. For example, the instruction CB 80 will clear bit 0 of register B.

## 3.3   Instruction Types

Microprocessor instructions can be divided broadly into the following types:

(a)  Data transfers. These may be between registers or between a register and a store location.

(b)  Arithmetic operations. These generally take one operand as the initial contents of the accumulator and leave the result also in the accumulator. The other operand may come from an internal register, from the instruction itself, or from the store.

(c)  Logical operations. These are similar to arithmetic operations with regard to the source and destination of the data, but the operations are logical functions performed on each bit of one operand and the corresponding bit of the other operand.

(d)  Incrementing and decrementing. These add one to or subtract one from the contents of an internal register or a store location.

(e)  Shifting and rotating. These operate on a single byte held in either a register or a store location. The rotate operations usually include the carry bit, but the Z80 instructions also allow rotation without the carry.

(f)  Branches. These allow the program to jump out of the normal sequence of instruction execution to some other part of the program if a certain condition is satisfied.

(g)  Stack operations. These can load the stack pointer and transfer data to and from the stack.

(h)  Miscellaneous. These control interrupts, individual flags and include the no operation instruction.

In the following sections instructions will be considered in more detail. A complete specification of all instructions which a particular microprocessor can execute is a complex document, since it must include not only a description of the data handling, but also the number of bytes in the instruction and the number of clock cycles required to fetch and execute it. It is necessary to know which flags may be altered and which are not affected, in order to make proper use of the branch instructions.

### 3.4    Data Transfer Instructions

These are of two types, Load and Store. Load instructions copy the contents of a store location or register into the accumulator or a second register. The data remains in the source, but the old information in the destination is written over and destroyed. When two registers are concerned the destination is usually given first followed by the source. Thus in the Z80 there is a set of instructions such as LD B,C which allows a byte from any 8-bit register to be copied into any other 8-bit register. This instruction copies the contents of C into B. The 6800 allows either accumulator, the stack pointer, or the index register to be loaded with immediate, direct, extended, or indexed addressing. The Z80 also allows any 8-bit register to be loaded with an immediate operand, or from a store location whose address is held in the HL register pair. The accumulator can be loaded as well from an address held in BC or DE. 16 bits can be loaded into either index register (IX or IY), SP, BC, DE, or HL using immediate or absolute addressing. The Z80 also enables the contents of registers to be interchanged; for example EX AF,AF′ exchanges the contents of the main accumulator and flag register with those of the corresponding alternative set. EXX′ performs the same function for the remaining registers B, C, D, E, H and L. There are also block move instructions which use registers HL to hold the source location, DE to hold the destination location, and BC to hold a byte count. When these registers have been loaded, the single instruction LDIR (Load, increment, and repeat) will continue to transfer bytes until the byte counter has reached zero. At each transfer the data pointers HL and DE are incremented and counter BC is decremented. For some applications other actions must be performed on the data between transfers; the instruction LDI (Load and increment) will then effect one data transfer and update the pointers. LDDR and LDD operate in a similar fashion, but work down the store instead of up the store, so that the data pointers are decremented after each transfer.

The 6502 has a single accumulator, two index registers, and a stack pointer which require a byte each and a program counter which holds two bytes. To compensate in part for the lack of extra registers the Accumulator can be loaded with the following address modes:

|  |  | Op. code for LDA | Op code for STA |
|---|---|---|---|
| (a) | Immediate | A9 | — |
| (b) | Zero page | A5 | 85 |
| (c) | Absolute | AD | 8D |
| (d) | Zero page, indexed with X reg. | B5 | 95 |
| (e) | Absolute, indexed with X reg. | BD | 9D |
| (f) | Absolute, indexed with Y reg. | B9 | 99 |
| (g) | Indexed, indirect | A1 | 81 |
| (h) | Indirect, indexed | B1 | 91 |

The X index register can be loaded with modes (a), (b), (c) and (f), and zero page, indexed with Y. The Y index register can be loaded with modes (a), (b), (c), (d) and (e). The stack pointer can only be loaded via the X register using the TXA instruction which copies the X register into the SP.

The following list gives the op. codes for some typical load instructions:

| 6800 | | *Address Mode* | | |
|---|---|---|---|---|
| *Mnemonic* | *Immed.* | *Direct* | *Index* | *Extended* |
| LDAA - | 86 | 96 | A6 | B6 |
| LDAB - | C6 | D6 | E6 | F6 |
| LDX - | CE | DE | EE | FE |
| LDS - | BE | 9E | AE | BE |

Here LDX and LDS load the index register and stack pointer.

| Z80 | | *Address Mode* | | | |
|---|---|---|---|---|---|
| *Mnemonic* | *Immed.* | *Abs.* | *Ind. X* | *Ind. Y* | *(HL)* |
| LD A, - | 3E | 3A | DD 7E | FD 7E | 7E |
| LD B, - | 06 | | DD 46 | FD 46 | 46 |
| LD C, - | 0E | | DD 4E | FD 4E | 4E |
| LD BC, - | 01 | ED 48 | | | |
| LD HL, - | 21 | 2A | | | |
| LD SP, - | 31 | ED 7B | | | |
| LD IX, - | DD 21 | DD 2A | | | |
| LD IY, - | FD 21 | FD 2A | | | |

Store instructions act in a manner similar to Load instructions, but in the reverse direction. One or two bytes from processor registers are copied to some location in the external store, destroying its previous contents. Some confusion is caused because 6800 and 6502 instructions use the word store whereas all Z80 transfers are called Load regardless of the direction of data flow. Since all the microprocessors we are concerned with are what are called 'Single-address' machines, that is they have space for only one address or operand in the instruction, they cannot encode a Store Accumulator instruction with immediate addressing since this would need one byte for the address and a further one for the operand. If we need to load a particular constant into some store location, it must first be loaded into an accumulator or other register and then transferred to the store.

Some typical store instructions are shown in the following table. The code for 6502 instructions is shown above alongside those for the Load instructions.

| 6800 | | Address Mode | |
| Mnemonic | Direct | Index | Extended |
| STAA - | 97 | A7 | B7 |
| STAB - | D7 | E7 | F7 |
| STX - | DF | EF | FF |
| STS - | 9F | AF | BF |

STX and STS store the index register and stack pointer. They use two store bytes to accommodate the 16-bit operand; these are stored in the location specified and the following byte.

| | | Addressing Mode | | | |
| Z80 | | Index | Index | | |
| Mnemonic | Abs. | IX | IY | (HL) | (BC) |
| LD -, A | 32 | DD 77 | FD 77 | 77 | 02 |
| LD -, B | – | DD 70 | FD 70 | 70 | – |
| LD -, HL | 22 | – | – | – | – |
| LD -, IX | DD 22 | – | – | – | – |
| LD -, IY | FD 22 | – | – | – | – |

## 3.5    Arithmetic Operations

Instructions in this category include:

> Add operand to accumulator contents, with or without carry
> Subtract, with or without carry
> Compare
> Test
> Complement
> Negate

For single-byte operands a plain ADD suffices, but when working with multiple-length operands, all bytes after the least significant will need to have the carry from the previous add operation added in. The ADC instruction effects this. A similar problem arises in subtraction where SUB and SBC instructions provide for the exclusion or inclusion of the carry (sometimes called the 'borrow bit' in subtraction). In order to save op. codes, the 6502 can perform only add and subtract with carry. To cope with this the carry bit must be cleared before using ADC for a two-byte add. The compare instruction subtracts the operand from the accumulator contents, but does not alter the contents of either. Its purpose is to update the flags for a subsequent branch instruction. Test performs the same function with the operand zero. Complement changes all ones in the byte to zero and all zeros to one. Negate generates –n from the value n in the operand byte using two's complement notation.

The following tables show typical instructions and their op. codes for addition and subtraction.

| *6800* | | *Address Mode* | | |
|--------|--------|--------|--------|--------|
| *Mnemonic* | *Immed.* | *Direct* | *Index* | *Extended* |
| ADDA | 8B | 9B | AB | BB |
| ADDB | CB | DB | EB | FB |
| ADCA | 89 | 99 | A9 | B9 |
| ADCB | C9 | D9 | E9 | F9 |
| SUBA | 80 | 90 | A0 | B0 |
| SUBB | C0 | D0 | E0 | F0 |
| SBCA | 82 | 92 | A2 | B2 |
| SBCB | C2 | D2 | E2 | F2 |

| *Z80* *Mnemonic* | *Op. Code* | *Address Mode* |
|------------------|------------|----------------|
| ADD A, B | 80 | Register |
| ADD A, C | 81 | Register |
| ADD A, (HL) | 86 | Register Indirect |
| ADD A, n | C6 | Immediate |
| ADC A, B | 88 | Register |
| ADC A, C | 89 | Register |
| ADC A, (HL) | 8E | Register Indirect |
| ADC A, n | CE | Immediate |
| ADD HL,BC | 09 | Register |
| ADD A, (IX+d) | DD 86 | Indexed |
| ADC A, (IX+d) | DD 8E | Indexed |
| SUB A, B | 90 | Register |
| SUB A, C | 91 | Register |
| SUB A, (HL) | 96 | Register Indirect |
| SUB A, n | D6 | Immediate |
| SUB A, (IX+d) | DD 96 | Indexed |
| SBC A, B | 98 | Register |
| SBC A, C | 99 | Register |
| SBC A, (HL) | 9E | Register Indirect |
| SBC A, n | DE | Immediate |
| SBC HL, BC | ED 42 | Register |
| SBC A, (IX+d) | DD 9E | Indexed |

All indexed and immediate op. codes are followed by one byte containing either the displacement or the immediate operand.

| 6502 Mnemonic | Op. Code | Addressing Mode |
|---|---|---|
| ADC #n | 69 | Immediate |
| ADC n | 65 | Zero Page |
| ADC nn | 6D | Absolute |
| ADC dd,X | 7D | Absolute Indexed |
| SBC #n | E9 | Immediate |
| SBC n | E5 | Zero Page |
| SBC nn | ED | Absolute |
| SBC dd,X | FD | Absolute Indexed |

### 3.6   Compare and Test Instructions

The Compare instruction subtracts the operand from the contents of an accumulator and updates the flags, but does not alter the accumulator contents. The test instruction for the 6800 performs the same action using an operand of zero.

Some typical instructions are given in the tables below.

| 6800 Mnemonic | Op. Code | Address Mode |
|---|---|---|
| CMPA #n | 81 | Immediate |
| CMPA n | 91 | Direct |
| CMPA n,X | A1 | Indexed |
| CMPA nn | B1 | Extended |
| CMPB #n | C1 | Immediate |
| CMPB n | D1 | Direct |
| CMPB n,X | E1 | Indexed |
| CMPB nn | F1 | Extended |
| TSTA | 4D | Inherent |
| TSTB | 5D | Inherent |
| TST n,X | 6D | Indexed |
| TST nn | 7D | Extended |
| CPX #nn | 8C | Immediate (16 bit) |
| CPX n | 9C | Direct |
| CPX n,X | AC | Indexed |
| CPX nn | BC | Extended |

Here CPX stands for Compare Index Register.

| Z80 Mnemonic | Op. Code | Address Mode |
|---|---|---|
| CP #n | FE | Immediate |
| CP B | B8 | Register |
| CP C | B9 | Register |
| CP (HL) | BE | Register Indirect |
| CP (IX+d) | DD BE | Indexed |

Here the operand is subtracted from the accumulator contents.

| 6502 Mnemonic | Op. Code | Address Mode |
|---|---|---|
| CMP #n | C9 | Immediate |
| CMP n | C5 | Zero Page |
| CMP nn | CD | Absolute |
| CMP n, X | D5 | Zero Page, Indexed |
| CMP nn, X | DD | Absolute Indexed |
| CPX #nn | E0 | Immediate (16 bit) |
| CPX n | E4 | Zero Page |
| CPX nn | EC | Absolute |
| CPY #nn | C0 | Immediate (16 bit) |
| CPY n | C4 | Zero Page |
| CPY nn | CC | Absolute |

In the above the CMP instruction compares the operand with the contents of the accumulator; CPX and CPY compare the operand with the contents of the X and Y index registers.

## 3.7 Complement and Negate Instructions

The Complement instruction changes the 1s in the operand into 0s and the 0s into 1s; Negate calculates the 2s complement of the operand, usually by taking the complement and adding one to it. The following tables give some typical complement and negate instructions.

| 6800 Mnemonic | Op. Code | Address Mode |
|---|---|---|
| COM n,X | 63 | Indexed |
| COM nn | 73 | Extended |
| COMA | 43 | Inherent |
| COMB | 53 | Inherent |
| NEG n,X | 60 | Indexed |
| NEG nn | 70 | Extended |
| NEGA | 40 | Inherent |
| NEGB | 50 | Inherent |

| Z80 Mnemonic | Op. Code | Address Mode |
|---|---|---|
| CPL | 2F | Inherent |
| NEG | ED 44 | Inherent |

The Z80 instructions operate only on the accumulator contents.

The 6502 has no instructions for complementing or negation.

### 3.8   Logical Operations

All logical operations are performed on individual bits of two operands, one being held in the accumulator and the other in another register, in the store or in the instructions. Thus bit 0 of the accumulator is taken with bit 0 of the other operand, bit 1 with bit 1, etc. If the two bits are labelled A and B and the result is called X, the consequence of the logical operations AND, OR, and EOR (exclusive OR) are shown in the following table.

| OR | | | AND | | | EOR | | |
|---|---|---|---|---|---|---|---|---|
| A | B | X | A | B | X | A | B | X |
| 0 | 0 | 0 | 0 | 0 | 0 | 0 | 0 | 0 |
| 0 | 1 | 1 | 0 | 1 | 0 | 0 | 1 | 1 |
| 1 | 0 | 1 | 1 | 0 | 0 | 1 | 0 | 1 |
| 1 | 1 | 1 | 1 | 1 | 1 | 1 | 1 | 0 |

Thus, if we have two bytes FO and AA the logical operations will have the following results:

| OR | AND | EOR |
|---|---|---|
| 11110000 | 11110000 | 11110000 |
| 10101010 | 10101010 | 10101010 |
| | | |
| 11111010 | 10100000 | 01011010 |

The following tables give some typical logical instructions.

| 6800 Mnemonic | Op. Code | Address Mode |
|---|---|---|
| ANDA #n | 84 | Immediate |
| ANDA n | 94 | Direct |
| ANDA n,X | A4 | Indexed |
| ANDA nn | B4 | Extended |
| ANDB #n | C4 | Immediate |
| ANDB n | D4 | Direct |
| ANDB n,X | E4 | Indexed |
| ANDB nn | F4 | Extended |
| EORA #n | 88 | Immediate |
| EORA n | 98 | Direct |
| EORA n,X | A8 | Indexed |
| EORA nn | B8 | Extended |
| EORB #n | C8 | Immediate |
| EORB n | D8 | Direct |
| EORB n,X | E8 | Indexed |
| EORB nn | F8 | Extended |
| ORAA #n | 8A | Immediate |
| ORAA n | 9A | Direct |
| ORAA n,X | AA | Indexed |
| ORAA nn | BA | Extended |
| ORAB #n | CA | Immediate |
| ORAB n | DA | Direct |
| ORAB n,X | EA | Indexed |
| ORAB nn | FA | Extended |

| Z80 Mnemonic | Op. Code | Address Mode |
|---|---|---|
| AND B | A0 | Register |
| AND C | A1 | Register |
| AND (HL) | A6 | Register Indirect |
| AND #n | E6 | Immediate |
| AND (IX+d) | DD A6 | Indexed |
| OR B | B0 | Register |
| OR C | B1 | Register |
| OR (HL) | B6 | Register Indirect |
| OR #n | F6 | Immediate |
| OR (IX+d) | DD B6 | Indexed |
| XOR B | A8 | Register |
| XOR C | A9 | Register |
| XOR (HL) | AE | Register Indirect |
| XOR #n | EE | Immediate |
| XOR (IX+d) | DD AE | Indexed |

In all of the Z80 instructions one operand is held in the accumulator; the op. code XOR is used for the exclusive OR.

| 6502 Mnemonic | Op. Code | Address Mode |
|---|---|---|
| AND #n | 29 | Immediate |
| AND n | 25 | Zero Page |
| AND nn | 2D | Absolute |
| AND nn, X | 3D | Indexed |
| ORA #n | 09 | Immediate |
| ORA n | 05 | Zero Page |
| ORA nn | 0D | Absolute |
| ORA nn,X | 1D | Indexed |
| EOR #n | 49 | Immediate |
| EOR nn | 4D | Absolute |
| EOR nn,X | 5D | Indexed |

In the 6502 instructions ORA denotes OR with accumulator and EOR the exclusive OR.

### 3.9   Instructions for Incrementing and Decrementing

These instructions are generally provided for both 8-bit and 16-bit operands. They are used in counting loops, time delay loops, and in the case of index registers in accessing sequentially the items in a block of data. One problem is that no action is taken on the flag bits with 16-bit operations on the Z80; this means that the index register may be used to access a block of data but not to determine when the loop has ended by checking whether the contents of the IR have reached zero. This problem does not arise with the 6800 or the 6502. Some typical instructions are shown in the table below.

| 6800 Mnemonic | Op. Code | Address Mode |
|---|---|---|
| INCA | 4C | Inherent |
| INCB | 5C | Inherent |
| INC d,X | 6C | Indexed |
| INC nn | 7C | Extended |
| DECA | 4A | Inherent |
| DECB | 5A | Inherent |
| DEC d,X | 6A | Indexed |
| DEC nn | 7A | Extended |
| INX | 08 | Inherent |
| DEX | 09 | Inherent |

Here INX and DEX operate on the index register.

| Z80 Mnemonic | Op. Code | Address Mode |
|---|---|---|
| INC A | 3C | Inherent |
| INC B | 04 | Inherent |
| INC (HL) | 34 | Register Indirect |
| INC (IX+d) | DD 34 | Indexed |
| INC BC | 03 | Inherent |
| INC IX | DD 23 | Inherent |
| DEC A | 3D | Inherent |
| DEC B | 05 | Inherent |
| DEC C | 0D | Inherent |
| DEC (HL) | 35 | Register Indirect |
| DEC (IX+d) | DD 35 | Indexed |
| DEC BC | 0B | Inherent |
| DEC IX | DD 28 | Inherent |

### 3.10 Instructions for Shifting and Rotating

In these instructions the contents of a register or a location in the store are moved one place left or right. In shifting, the bit pushed out is loaded into the carry flag, and the incoming bit loaded into the empty place is usually 0. Shifting is used to multiply or divide by 2; multiplication requires a left shift and division a right shift. A right shift performed on a positive number gives the correct result, but a shift with a 0 fed in at the left gives an incorrect result with a negative operand. In this case the new bit must be 1 to retain the negative sign. Thus most microprocessors have an Arithmetic Shift Right instruction which copies the sign bit back into the left-hand place as well as shifting it one place right. All other bits are moved one place right. The scheme is shown below. This procedure gives the correct result for both positive and negative numbers.

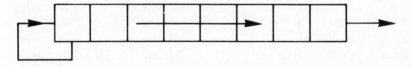

Shifting is used also to allow each bit of a number to be examined in turn as it appears in either the carry flag or the most significant (left-hand) place. After repeated shifts the original data disappears; if this must be retained a rotate instruction can be used in which the bit pushed out at one end of the register is put back in at the other end. The rotation usually includes the carry bit but the Z80 allows also for rotation without the carry.

Some typical instructions are shown in the tables below.

| 6800 Mnemonic | Op. Code | Address Mode | Action |
|---|---|---|---|
| ROLA | 49 | Inherent | Rotate Left |
| ROLB | 59 | Inherent | Rotate Left |
| ROL n,X | 69 | Indexed | Rotate Left |
| ROL nn | 79 | Extended | Rotate Left |
| RORA | 46 | Inherent | Rotate Right |
| RORB | 56 | Inherent | Rotate Right |
| ROR n,X | 66 | Indexed | Rotate Right |
| ROR nn | 76 | Extended | Rotate Right |
| ASLA | 48 | Inherent | Arithmetic Shift Left |
| ASLB | 58 | Inherent | Arithmetic Shift Left |
| ASL n,X | 68 | Indexed | Arithmetic Shift Left |
| ASL nn | 78 | Extended | Arithmetic Shift Left |
| ASRA | 47 | Inherent | Arithmetic Shift Right |
| ASRB | 57 | Inherent | Arithmetic Shift Right |
| ASR n,X | 67 | Indexed | Arithmetic Shift Right |
| ASR nn | 77 | Extended | Arithmetic Shift Right |
| LSRA | 44 | Inherent | Logical Shift Right |
| LSRB | 54 | Inherent | Logical Shift Right |
| LSR n,X | 64 | Indexed | Logical Shift Right |
| LSR nn | 74 | Extended | Logical Shift Right |

| Z80 Mnemonic | Op. Code | Address Mode | Action |
|---|---|---|---|
| RL A | 17 | Inherent | Rotate Left |
| RL B | CB 10 | Inherent | Rotate Left |
| RL (HL) | CB 16 | Indirect | Rotate Left |
| RL (IX+d) | DD CB d 16 | Indexed | Rotate Left |
| RLC A | 07 | Inherent | Rotate Left Circular |
| RLC B | CB 00 | Inherent | Rotate Left Circular |
| RR A | 1F | Inherent | Rotate Right |
| RR B | CB 18 | Inherent | Rotate Right |
| RRC A | 0F | Inherent | Rotate Right Circular |
| RRC B | CB 08 | Inherent | Rotate Right Circular |
| SLA A | CB 27 | Inherent | Shift Left Arithmetic |
| SLA B | CB 20 | Inherent | Shift Left Arithmetic |
| SRA A | CB 2F | Inherent | Shift Right Arithmetic |
| SRA B | CB 28 | Inherent | Shift Right Arithmetic |
| SRL A | CB 3F | Inherent | Shift Right Logical |
| SRL B | CB 38 | Inherent | Shift Right Logical |

| 6502 Mnemonic | Op. Code | Address Mode | Action |
|---|---|---|---|
| ASL A | 0A | Inherent | |
| ASL n | 06 | Zero Page | Arithmetic |
| ASL nn | 0E | Absolute | Shift |
| ASL n,X | 16 | Zero Page Indexed | Left |
| ASL nn, X | 1E | Absolute Indexed | |
| LSR A | 4A | Inherent | Logical |
| LSR n | 46 | Zero Page | Shift Right |
| ROL A | 2A | Inherent | |
| ROL n | 26 | Zero Page | Rotate |
| ROL nn | 2E | Absolute | Left |
| ROR A | 6A | Inherent | |
| ROR n | 66 | Zero Page | Rotate |
| ROR nn | 6E | Absolute | Right |
| ROR nn,X | 7E | Absolute Indexed | |

The ROL and ROR instructions of the 6502 both include the carry bit in the circulation path.

## 3.11 Branch Instructions

One of the features which gives modern computers their extraordinary power to calculate and handle information is the capacity for altering their actions in accordance with the result obtained at any stage of the calculation. A set of branch instructions is provided for this purpose. Nearly all of these are more exactly called *Conditional Branch Instructions*.

At machine code level they give the computer two options: to execute the next instruction if a certain condition is not satisfied, or to execute some other instruction if it is satisfied. This allows the program to leave the current sequence of instructions and to start executing another set of instructions somewhere else in the store. The action depends on the result of the previous instruction which passed through the arithmetic and logic unit and updated the flags. Some typical conditions which can be specified are

Result Zero
Result Non-Zero
Result Positive
Result Negative
Carry Set
Carry Clear
Overflow Set
Overflow Clear

For completeness, an unconditional branch is usually included. This acts in the same way as the GOTO statement in BASIC. Some microprocessor instruction sets use the name Branch where relative addressing is used and Jump where the instruction contains an absolute address. Branches are normally two-byte instructions and use relative addressing, with a displacement or offset held in the second byte. The Z80 instructions set is unusual in that branches are called Jump Relative (JR) and in addition to relative addressing, there is provision for absolute addressing; this requires three bytes, with a 16-bit address contained in the last two bytes. It is convenient to include in this group of instructions those which invoke subroutines. These have a variety of titles including *Jump to Subroutine* (JSR), *Branch to Subroutine* (BSR) and *CALL*. They copy the contents of the PC (the return address) onto the stack before replacing them by the address of the first byte of the subroutine. At the end of the subroutine a *Return from Subroutine* (RTS or RET) instruction pulls the return address from the stack and loads it into the PC, so allowing the microprocessor to continue executing the main program from the instruction below the Jump to Subroutine. The Z80 has a set of conditional Call instructions which are executed only if specified conditions are satisfied, similar to those for the branch instructions. Thus one can call a subroutine if the carry bit is set, if the last result was zero or negative, etc. Conditional Return from Subroutine instructions are also provided so that one can return from a subroutine only if the carry bit is set, etc. Conditional Call and Conditional Return are features not provided on many larger computers.

The following tables show some typical branch and jump instructions.

| 6800 Mnemonic | Op. Code | Address Mode | Test on Flags |
|---|---|---|---|
| BRA | 20 | Relative | None |
| BCC | 24 | Relative | C = 0 |
| BEQ | 27 | Relative | Z = 1 |
| BNE | 26 | Relative | Z = 0 |
| BMI | 2B | Relative | N = 1 |
| BVC | 28 | Relative | V = 0 |
| BPL | 2A | Relative | N = 0 |
| BSR | 8D | Relative | None |
| JMP | 6E | Indexed | None |
| JMP | 7E | Extended | None |
| JSR | AD | Indexed | None |
| JSR | BD | Extended | None |
| RTS | 39 | Indirect | None |

| Z80 Mnemonic | Op. Code | Address Mode | Test on Flags |
|---|---|---|---|
| JR | 18 | Relative | None |
| JR Z | 28 | Relative | Z = 1 |
| JR C | 38 | Relative | C = 1 |
| JR NZ | 20 | Relative | Z = 0 |
| JR NC | 30 | Relative | C = 0 |
| JP nn | C3 | Absolute | None |
| JP (HL) | E9 | Indirect | None |
| JP Z,nn | CA | Absolute | Z = 1 |
| JP NZ,nn | C2 | Absolute | Z = 0 |
| JP C,nn | DA | Absolute | C = 1 |
| JP NC,nn | D2 | Absolute | C = 0 |
| JP PE,nn | EA | Absolute | P = 1 |
| JP PO,nn | E2 | Absolute | P = 0 |
| JP P,nn | F2 | Absolute | S = 0 |
| JP M,nn | FA | Absolute | S = 1 |
| CALL nn | CD | Absolute | None |
| CALL Z,nn | CC | Absolute | Z = 1 |
| CALL NZ,nn | C4 | Absolute | Z = 0 |
| CALL C,nn | DC | Absolute | C = 1 |
| RET | C9 | Indirect | None |
| RET Z,nn | C8 | Indirect | Z = 1 |
| RET NZ,nn | C0 | Indirect | Z = 0 |
| RET C,nn | D8 | Indirect | C = 1 |

| 6502 Mnemonic | Op. Code | Address Mode | Test on Flags |
|---|---|---|---|
| BNE | D0 | Relative | Z = 0 |
| BEQ | F0 | Relative | Z = 1 |
| BPL | 10 | Relative | N = 0 |
| BCC | 90 | Relative | C = 0 |
| BMI | 30 | Relative | N = 1 |
| BVC | 50 | Relative | V = 0 |
| BVS | 70 | Relative | V = 1 |
| BCS | B0 | Relative | C = 1 |
| JMP nn | 4C | Absolute | None |
| JMP (nn) | 6C | Absolute, Indirect | None |
| JSR nn | 20 | Absolute | None |
| RTS | 60 | Indirect | None |

In the tables above the Return from Subroutine instructions are shown as indirectly addressed since the effective address is held in the stack at a location pointed to by the Stack Pointer.

## 3.12 Stack Operations

Stack instructions allow the Stack Pointer to be loaded at the start of the program, to be incremented and decremented and, in the Z80, to be used in some 16-bit arithmetic. Apart from this the only other operations allowed are pushing items onto the stack or pulling (popping) them off it. When executing a Jump to Subroutine instruction the processor will automatically push the return link onto the stack, and pull it off when returning from the subroutine. Any other items which are stored temporarily on the stack must be controlled by the programmer.

Of the three microprocessors discussed, the 6502 has much the smallest set of stack instructions. These enable the contents of the accumulator and the program status register (flag register) to be put onto the stack or removed from it. There is no facility for loading the SP directly; an address can, however, be loaded into the Y register and then transferred to the SP.

The following tables show some typical stack instructions.

| 6800 Mnemonic | Op. Code | Action |
|---|---|---|
| LDS | 8E | Load SP Immediate |
| LDS | 9E | Load SP Direct |
| LDS | AE | Load SP Indexed |
| LDS | BE | Load SP Extended |
| PSHA | 36 | Push Acc. A onto Stack |
| PSHB | 37 | Push Acc. B onto Stack |
| PULA | 32 | Pull Data from Stack to Acc. A |
| PULB | 33 | Pull Data from Stack to Acc. B |

| Z80 Mnemonic | Op. Code | Action |
|---|---|---|
| LD SP, #nn | 31 | Load SP Immediate |
| LD SP, (nn) | ED 78 | Load SP Absolute |
| LD SP, HL | F9 | Load SP from HL |
| PUSH AF | F5 | Push A and F onto Stack |
| PUSH HL | E5 | Push H and L onto Stack |
| PUSH IX | DD E5 | Push IX onto Stack |
| POP AF | F1 | Pull Data from Stack to A and F |
| POP HL | E1 | Pull Data from Stack to H and L |
| POP IX | DD 22 | Pull Data from Stack to IX reg. |

| *6502*<br>*Mnemonic* | *Op.*<br>*Code* | *Action* |
|---|---|---|
| PHA | 48 | Push Acc. onto Stack |
| PHP | 08 | Push PSR onto Stack |
| PLA | 68 | Pull Data from Stack to Acc. |
| PLP | 28 | Pull Data from Stack to PSR |
| TXS | 9A | Transfer IX reg. to SP |

In the 6502 instructions, PSR denotes the Processor Status Register (Flag Register). The initial address loaded into the Stack Pointer must always be chosen so that the Stack can operate in an area of RAM. It must be at the top end of the area allocated since the stack normally grows downwards, that is each new item is loaded at an address one below that which holds the previous item.

### 3.13  Miscellaneous Instructions

It is convenient to include in this category instructions which control interrupts and the state of the flags. All microprocessors have an NOP (No Operation) instruction which has no action on the processor but advances the program counter to point to the next instruction. It is used in timing loops for adding a few microseconds to the time taken to execute a loop.

All three microprocessors described here have a maskable interrupt line, that is a line which can be made active or disabled by program. When power is first applied this is always disabled so that the various registers and peripheral packages can be set up without interference. After initialisation, the interrupt line can be enabled. In addition to this facility the Z80 has three other instructions which prescribe in what manner the interrupt line acts.

All three microprocessors have provision for performing decimal arithmetic on BCD numbers; in the 6800 and Z80 this requires a DAA (Decimal Add Adjust) instruction to follow each addition to convert the format to BCD. The processor then regards each byte as two BCD digits. The 6502 has a similar facility, but it is invoked by the instruction SED (Set Decimal Model) and will stay in force until cancelled by the instruction CLD (Clear Decimal Mode).

The programmer has some access to the flag bits: in the Z80 only to the Carry bit, in the 6502 and the 6800 to the Carry and Overflow bits.

The Z80 also has a set of eight RESTART instructions which are single-byte calls to addresses 0000, 0008, 0010, 0018, etc. These can be used to call quickly a number of frequently used subroutines, or to allow the device requesting an interrupt to identify itself and call its service routine.

When using microprocessors to control plant and machinery it may be necessary to set, clear, or test any particular bit held in a register, corresponding to some alarm line or sensor output. The Z80 makes special provision for this in a set of 240 instructions. These allow access to internal registers A, B, C, D, E, H,

L and external locations addressed either via HL, or either index register. Any bit of these registers can be set, cleared, or tested. The test leaves a 1 in the Zero Flag if the bit is clear.

The following tables show some typical instructions.

| 6800 Mnemonic | Op. Code | Action |
|---|---|---|
| CLI | 0E | Clear Interrupt Mask |
| SEI | 0F | Set Interrupt Mask |
| CLC | 0C | Clear Carry Bit |
| SEC | 0D | Set Carry Bit |
| CLV | 0A | Clear Overflow Bit |
| SEV | 0B | Set Overflow Bit |
| DAA | 19 | Decimal Add Adjust |
| NOP | 01 | No Operation |

| Z80 Mnemonic | Op. Code | Action |
|---|---|---|
| SCF | 37 | Set Carry Flag |
| CCF | 3F | Complement Carry Flag |
| EI | FB | Enable Interrupts |
| DI | F3 | Disable Interrupts |
| IM0 | ED 46 | Set Interrupt Mode 0 |
| IM1 | ED 56 | Set Interrupt Mode 1 |
| IM2 | ED 5E | Set Interrupt Mode 2 |
| DAA | 27 | Decimal Add Adjust |
| NOP | 00 | No Operation |
| RST 00 | C7 | Call to location 0000 |
| RST 08 | CF | Call to location 0008 |
| RES 2,C | CB 91 | Reset Bit 2 of Reg. C |
| SET 4,H | CB E4 | Set Bit 4 of Reg. H |
| BIT 3,D | CB 5A | Test Bit 3 of Reg. D |

| 6502 Mnemonic | Op. Code | Action |
|---|---|---|
| CLI | 58 | Clear Interrupt Mask |
| SEI | 78 | Set Interrupt Mask |
| CLC | 18 | Clear Carry Bit |
| SEC | 38 | Set Carry Bit |
| CLV | B8 | Clear Carry Bit |
| SED | F8 | Set Decimal Mode |
| CLD | D8 | Clear Decimal Mode |
| NOP | EA | No Operation |

# 4 Subroutines and the Use of the Stack

## 4.1 Subroutines

When planning programs we generally find that there are some small tasks which need to be performed frequently and if the instructions for these are written out in full each time they are needed the program becomes large and unwieldy. Much time and program space could be saved if it were possible to write the program for each task once only, and execute it repeatedly when required. Since this is such a frequent requirement, all microprocessors make provision for doing so. The program for each task is arranged as a *Subroutine* and stored outside the normal sequence of the main program. The subroutine is a normal segment of program but in order that the computer can return to the main program after executing it, the subroutine must end with a special *Return from Subroutine* (RTS or RET) instruction.

In order to execute the subroutine the main program must contain an instruction such as

> Jump to Subroutine (JSR)
> Branch to Subroutine (BSR)
> Call Subroutine (CALL)

This is usually a three-byte instruction which contains the 16-bit address of the first byte of the subroutine in the last two bytes (absolute addressing). However, the 6800 also allows indexed addressing, and in the case of BSR relative addressing. When executing the Jump to Subroutine the processor first pushes the contents of the program counter onto the stack (the *Return Link*) and then copies the address in the instruction into the program counter and fetches the next instruction. This will be the first instruction in the subroutine. At the end of the subroutine the RTS instruction will pull the address from the top of the stack and copy it into the program counter. This is the *Return Link* which points to the next instruction in the main program. The processor will then resume the main program at the instruction below the Jump to Subroutine instruction.

As an example we use the 6800 code with a main program starting in location 0100 and the subroutine starting in location 0200, and trace the contents of PC, SP and stack.

| Main Program | | | | Subroutine | |
|---|---|---|---|---|---|
| | Location | Code | | Location | Code |
| XXX | 0100 | XX | SUB: LDA NUM | 0200 | XX |
| XXX | 0101 | XX | XXX | 0201 | XX |
| JSR SUB | 0102 | BD | XXX | 0202 | XX |
| – | 0103 | 02 | – | – | – |
| – | 0104 | 00 | – | – | – |
| Return Link | 0105 | XX | RTS | 0230 | 39 |
| | 0106 | XX | | | |

### Executing JSR

| PC = 0105 | Stack | | PC = 0200 | Stack | |
|---|---|---|---|---|---|
| | 107F | – | | 107F | 01 |
| SP = 107F | 107E | – | SP = 107D | 107E | 05 |
| | 107D | – | | 107D | – |
| | 107C | – | | 107C | – |

(a) Initial State      (b) Return Link on Stack, PC loaded
Stack empty           with Subroutine address

### Executing RTS

| Return Link | PC = 0105 | Stack | |
|---|---|---|---|
| | | 107F | 01 |
| | SP = 107F | 107E | 05 |
| | | 107D | – |

(c) Return Link pulled from stack and loaded into PC. Stack pointer returned to
    initial state

We assume that the stack pointer is initially set to 107F. When starting to execute the JSR instruction the PC points to the next program byte in location 0105. The PC contents are then loaded onto the stack and the stack pointer decremented twice to 107D. The new PC address (0200) can then be fetched from the instruction, and loaded into the PC. The next instruction will then be fetched from the subroutine which starts at this address 0200. At the end of the subroutine the RTS instruction will pull the return link 0105 from the stack and load it into the PC. The SP will return to its original value when the JSR was executed, and the next instruction, fetched from 0105, will resume execution of the main program.

The return link is stored outside both the main program and the subroutine, and clearly the same mechanism can be used repeatedly to call the subroutine from any point in the main program as many times as required. A further facility which this mechanism provides is the ability to 'nest' subroutines. This means that a subroutine can call another subroutine, and the return links will be held on the stack in the correct order to return finally to the main program. The only limit to the depth of this nesting is the amount of storage provided for the stack.

## 4.2   Saving and Passing Variables

The main program and all subroutines must use the same set of processor registers. Thus when calling a subroutine it is important to ensure that the contents of any registers used by the subroutine are saved if they are required for subsequent processing in the main program. The most convenient place to store them is the stack, since moving data onto and off the stack needs only a single-byte instruction, whereas using external RAM needs at least two-byte instructions.

In the Z80 registers are moved to the stack in pairs, so that if registers B and C are to be used their contents can be saved and restored by starting the subroutine with the instruction

PUSH BC

and ending it with
POP BC RET

The accumulators in the 6800 are moved separately so that if their contents are to be saved two instructions are needed. The subroutine can be started with

PSH A<br>PSH B

and ended with

PUL B<br>PUL A<br>RTS

Note that the order of the accumulators is reversed when pulling the data off the stack, since this operates as a Last In First Out store. It is important that the number of Push instructions should equal the number of Pull instructions, otherwise the RTS instruction at the end of the subroutine will not extract the correct return link.

A frequent requirement when using subroutines is the interchange of data between the main program and the subroutine. The accumulator is the most convenient storage register for this purpose, but other registers such as index registers can be used if they are not needed in the subroutine. If more data is to be transferred, the stack is the most convenient storage area to use.

The Z80 is particularly convenient for data interchange since in addition to the accumulator, registers B, C, D, E and possibly H and L can be used as temporary stores.

## 4.3    Subroutines and Program Subdivision

When programs of any significant size are being planned, it is essential to divide the complete task into small modules, each of which can be specified separately, and thus written and tested separately. When these individual segments have been checked, they can be combined in stages into the complete program required. Any attempt to write the program in one continuous sequence is almost certain to produce errors which may be very difficult to find and correct. Writing and testing each module on its own is much easier if it is written as a subroutine. A very small main program can then be written to test it; this need only supply some data and make provision for checking the output of the subroutine.

The final program will then consist of a small main program which may perform minor tasks like initialising registers, and will then call the various subroutines which comprise the bulk of the program. This method of constructing programs is also most convenient when they are to be modified or extended. If they have been adequately subdivided it should be possible to do this by replacing subroutines or adding new ones. When altering a large program which has not been subdivided it is very difficult to ensure that a change made in one part of the program does not have unforeseen effects on some quite different part.

Where program writing is a regular rather than a 'one-off' activity there is a further advantage in dividing programs into small subroutines; many of these perform tasks which are required in many applications and one can soon build up a library of them which will form the basis of many future programs. Since these will already have been tested, the task of program development can be materially shortened in this way.

# 5 Basic Algorithms

## 5.1 Addition Programs

One of the simplest operations often needed in a microprocessor program is to add together two bytes held in the writable store and put the sum also into the store. This can only be done using the accumulator, so that the procedure becomes

> Load Accumulator from NUM1
> Add to Accumulator NUM2
> Store Accumulator in SUM

Here NUM1 and NUM2 are the addresses of the two bytes to be added and SUM the address allocated for the sum.

When translating this into machine code, we look for the smallest program which will execute in the shortest time. This means using page zero for the data, where there are special instructions for doing so, since these occupy fewer program bytes and need fewer clock cycles for execution. Thus, as a general rule, data in the 6800 and 6502 is held in storage page 0 (bytes 00 to FF hexadecimal). No page zero instructions are provided for the Z80 and some interrupt vectors are located in this area. Also when the Z80 starts operating after the power is switched on and the RESET pin has been pulsed, it fetches its first instruction from location 0000. Thus the program ROM must be located at the bottom of the storage space and the RAM holding data must be at a higher address, perhaps A000 and above.

Thus if the two bytes to be added are in locations 05 and 06 and the sum is to be put into location 0A, the program for a 6800 would be

| Instruction | Code | Comment |
|---|---|---|
| LDAA 05 | 96 05 | Fetch NUM1 |
| ADDA 06 | 9B 06 | Add NUM2 |
| STAA 0A | 97 0A | Store sum in 0A |

The program needs only one accumulator for this calculation. Here we have used accumulator A.

In the 6502 instruction set the only add operation is Add with Carry, so that when performing a two-byte add without carry we must first clear the carry bit. The 6502 program is thus

| Instruction | Code | Comment |
|---|---|---|
| CLC | 18 | Clear Carry Bit |
| LDA 05 | A5 05 | Fetch NUM1 |
| ADC 06 | 65 06 | Add NUM2 |
| STA 0A | 85 0A | Store sum in 0A |

In both the above programs the absolute addresses of the data (05 and 06) are held in the second bytes of the Load and Add instructions; the programs would be just as short and as quick to run wherever in page 0 the data was held. This is not the case with the Z80; the most compact program uses the HL register pair as a data pointer. This is initially loaded with the address of the first number, and then incremented by a single-byte instruction to point first to the other number and then to the location allocated for the sum. Thus for the shortest Z80 program we need to lay the data out in the available storage space in the correct order. This is a restriction not imposed by the other two microprocessors, but it does lead to compact programs. Also we do not suffer a penalty in the need for more program storage if the data is not in page zero. We will assume that the two numbers and the sum are in locations A000, A001 and A002. A suitable Z80 program would then be

| Instruction | Code | Comment |
|---|---|---|
| LD HL, A000 | 21 00 A0 | Load address of NUM 1 |
| LD A, (HL) | 7E | Fetch NUM 1 |
| INC HL | 23 | Increment address |
| ADD A, (HL) | 86 | Add NUM 2 |
| INC HL | 23 | Increment address |
| LD (HL), A | 77 | Store sum in A002 |

Note that all addresses in the Z80 are encoded with the lower byte first, so that the address A000 in the first instruction is encoded as 00 A0.

Although these very simple programs are often needed, and may be worth writing as subroutines, they can cause errors since they do not check for an over-flow. In many on-line applications this may not matter, because we know the characteristics of the transducers which generate NUM 1 and NUM 2 and the maximum value of their outputs. We can then scale these numbers so that no overflow occurs. It is easiest to cope with a possible overflow if the numbers are unsigned, by adding the carry digit into a previously cleared byte. We then generate a 16-bit sum with this byte as the most significant one and the sum as the least significant. If the numbers are signed we can try adding them using one of the above programs. If this causes an overflow, we can extend the numbers to two bytes and use one of the following programs.

## 5.2    16-bit Addition

Programs for adding numbers consisting of two or more bytes are similar to those above, but when adding higher-order bytes we must also add in the carry from the previous addition. With the 6800 and the 6502 only 8-bit arithmetic is possible, so we add the two bytes separately. With the Z80, 16-bit addition and subtraction is provided between some register pairs; we can add to or subtract from the contents of HL the contents of BC, DE, HL or SP.

A program for the 6800 with NUM 1 in 05 (MS byte) and 06 (LS byte), NUM 2 in 06 and 07, and the sum loaded into 0A and 0B is shown below.

| Instruction | Code | Comment |
|---|---|---|
| LDA A NUM 1 L | 96 06 | Fetch low byte of NUM 1 |
| ADD A NUM 2 L | 9B 08 | Add low byte of NUM 2 |
| STA A SUM L | 97 0B | Store sum in low byte of SUM |
| LDA A NUM 1 H | D6 05 | Fetch high byte of NUM 1 |
| ADC A NUM 2 H | D9 07 | Add with carry high byte of NUM 2 |
| STA A SUM H | D7 0A | Store sum in high byte of SUM |

In this microprocessor the LDA instruction does not affect the carry bit; this is set or cleared by the ADD instruction and is added in by the ADC instruction.

A similar program can be used with the 6502; the only changes (apart from different op. codes) are that we must start with CLC to clear the carry bit, we must use ADC in place of ADD, and we do not need to specify which accumulator to use.

The Z80 enables us to perform the 16-bit addition directly, using the HL register pair as an accumulator. We assume that NUM 1 is loaded into A000 and A001, NUM 2 into A002 and A003, with A004 and A005 reserved for the sum. When coding the instruction we specify only the address of the first byte of the number, which must be the low byte. The Z80 stores double-length numbers in the same way as 16-bit addresses: low bytes first. Thus our first instruction is LD BC, (A000). This loads the first byte at A000 into C and the second byte at A001 into B. In order to have the 16-bit number with its most significant bit at the left or high-order end of B and its least significant bit on the right of C, we must load the high byte into B and the low byte into C. Consequently the LS byte of NUM 1 must be in A000 and the MS byte in A001. The register pair BC will then hold the 16-bit number in the correct order. The layout is shown below.

|  | Register B |  |  |  |  |  |  |  |  | Register C |  |  |  |  |  |  |  |
|---|---|---|---|---|---|---|---|---|---|---|---|---|---|---|---|---|---|
| Bit | 7 | 6 | 5 | 4 | 3 | 2 | 1 | 0 | Bit | 7 | 6 | 5 | 4 | 3 | 2 | 1 | 0 |

Register Pair BC

| Bit | 15 | 14 | 13 | 12 | 11 | 10 | 9 | 8 | Bit | 7 | 6 | 5 | 4 | 3 | 2 | 1 | 0 |
|---|---|---|---|---|---|---|---|---|---|---|---|---|---|---|---|---|---|
|  | NUM 1 H Stored in A001 |  |  |  |  |  |  |  |  | NUM 1 L Stored in A000 |  |  |  |  |  |  |  |

The program can then be

| Instruction | Code | Comment |
|---|---|---|
| LD BC, (A000) | ED 48 00 A0 | Move NUM 1 to BC |
| LD HL, (A002) | 2A 02 A0 | Move NUM 2 to HL |
| ADD HL, BC | 09 | Add BC to HL |
| LD (A004), HL | 22 04 A0 | Store HL in SUM |

In this program registers B and H hold the most significant or high byte of the double-length numbers, and registers C and L hold the least significant or low bytes. Only 11 bytes of program are needed compared with 12 bytes for the 6800 program and the data can be loaded anywhere in the address space, whereas the 6800 data must be on page 0. If the data is in addresses above this, an extra 6 bytes are needed for extended addressing.

### 5.3  Subtraction

Programs for 8-bit subtraction are similar to those for addition, the only change needed being in the op. code. As with addition, numbers can be subtracted only from the accumulator, and the result will be left in the accumulator. The only caution needed is with the 6502. Since there are no ADD or SUB instructions, only ADC and SBC, bringing the carry bit into the operation, the carry must be cleared before adding. Since SBC complements the carry bit, this must be set before subtraction. Unless this is done an extra bit will be added to the result or subtracted from it. Thus we must start addition programs with CLC and subtraction with SEC.

16-bit subtractions resemble 16-bit additions with the 6800 in that the least significant byte must use the SUB instruction and the higher-order byte must use SBC. Thus the program for 16-bit addition listed in section 5.2 can be changed into a program for 16-bit subtraction by changing ADD to SUB and ADC to SBC.

A similar change in the program for the 6502 will produce a 16-bit subtraction, but as with the program for 8-bit subtraction the carry bit must be set before subtracting the low-order bytes.

The program for 16-bit addition with the Z80 needs a little more adjustment to produce a subtraction program since there is no SUB instruction which operates on register pairs, only SBC. Thus the carry bit must be cleared before the subtraction. There is no specific instruction for this but one can set the carry bit (SCF) and then complement it with CCF. However, a logical operation such as OR A will clear the carry bit with a single one-byte instruction, and is generally used. Thus using immediate operands a program for 16-bit subtraction could be

| Instruction | Code | Comment |
|---|---|---|
| OR A | B7 | OR A to clear carry bit |
| LD HL, A7B9 | 21 B9 A7 | Put A7B9 into HL |
| LD BC, 1B3D | 01 3D 1B | Put 1B3D into BC |
| SBC HL, BC | ED 42 | Subtract BC from HL |
| LD (A010), HL | 22 10 A0 | Store result in A010 and A011 |

The result of this will be 7C in A010 and 8C in A011, giving a 16-bit difference of 8C7C.

## 5.4 Decimal Arithmetic

Microprocessor applications are often concerned with collecting data from human operators and delivering output for them to some digital display. In these systems the data will be in decimal notation, usually encoded in BCD format. When the data processing involves relatively simple calculations it may be an advantage to keep the data in BCD format and perform decimal arithmetic on it. Because this is a frequent requirement, most microprocessor manufacturers provide some facility for decimal arithmetic. The 6800 and Z80 have a DAA (Decimal Adjust Accumulator) instruction which can be used after each addition to correct the result when BCD format is used. The following program can be used with the 6800.

| Instruction | Code | Comment |
|---|---|---|
| LDA A NUM 1 | 96 05 | Fetch first number |
| ADD A NUM 2 | 9B 06 | Add second number |
| DAA | 19 | Decimal adjust |
| STA A SUM | 97 0A | Store result in SUM |

Here NUM 1 and NUM 2 are held in 05 and 06 and the result in 0A.

The DAA instruction applies only to Accumulator A, so that we must use this for the calculation. Subtraction is a little more complicated; since the DAA normally follows addition we must use 10's complement arithmetic and add the complement of NUM 2 to NUM 1. The complement in BCD is obtained by subtracting NUM 2 from 100. Thus a 6800 program for decimal subtraction could be

| Instruction | Code | Comment |
|---|---|---|
| LDA A #9A | 86 9A | Load 100 into Accumulator A |
| SUB A NUM 2 | 90 06 | Subtract NUM 2 |
| ADD A NUM 1 | 9B 05 | Add NUM 1 |
| DAA | 19 | Decimal adjust |
| STA A DIFF | 97 0A | Store result in DIFF |

Here NUM 1 and NUM 2 are held in locations 05 and 06 and the result in 0A. If NUM 1 and NUM 2 are 53 and 16, the result is 37. However if the numbers are reversed, (NUM 1 – NUM 2) is negative and it will appear in 10's complement form as 63. In this notation all numbers below 50 are positive, and 50 and above represent negative numbers. Similarly in hexadecimal notation, all numbers below 80 are positive, and 80 and above represent negative numbers. To find the magnitude of the negative number 63 we subtract it from 100, giving –37 as expected. BCD coding is clearly not as efficient as the normal binary code since the largest unsigned decimal number we can represent with 8 bits is 99 compared with 255 in binary.

Similar programs can be written for the Z80. The following will handle decimal addition.

| Instruction | Code | Comment |
|---|---|---|
| LD A, 46 | 3E 46 | Load 46 into Register A |
| LD B, 28 | 06 28 | Load 28 into Register B |
| ADD A, B | 80 | Add B to A |
| DAA | 27 | Decimal adjust |
| LD (1000), A | 32 00 10 | Store result in 1000 |

This program adds the immediate operands 46 and 28 and puts the result into location 1000. After running the program this will contain 74. A similar program will perform subtraction:

| Instruction | Code | Comment |
|---|---|---|
| LD A, 46 | 3E 46 | Load 46 into Register A |
| LD B, 28 | 06 28 | Load 28 into Register B |
| SUB B | 90 | Subtract B from A |
| DAA | 27 | Decimal adjust |
| LD (1000), A | 32 00 10 | Store result in 1000 |

This subtracts 28 from 46 and gives the expected result of 18. If the number 28 is changed to 68 the result will be 78. Being over 49 this represents a negative number which is – (100 – 78) = –22.

The 6502 also has facilities for decimal arithmetic, but instead of having to follow each arithmetic operation by the instruction DAA decimal mode can be entered by executing the instruction SED (Set Decimal Mode). All subsequent operations will then be performed in decimal, until the instructions CLD (Clear Decimal Mode) is executed.

## 5.5   Multiple Addition

A frequent requirement in control applications is to add together a set of readings to determine their average. For the present we concentrate on the program needed for addition. Since we have to access in sequence a set of numbers already loaded into the store it is convenient to use a program loop in which the data is addressed via the index register. In the following program Accumulator A is initially cleared and each data item is added into it. The same instruction can be used for each item, by incrementing the index register after each addition. We shall obviously generate a sum much larger than we can store in one byte, so that we must make provision for a double-length sum. This is done by clearing Accumulator B initially and adding any carry bits into it. At the end of the addition this will hold the high byte of the sum and Accumulator A will hold the low byte.

One method of coping with the carry bits would be to test the carry bit after each addition, and if it has been set to increment Accumulator B. This is satisfactory but the program can be shortened if we can avoid the branch instruction and those associated with it. This can be done by always adding in the carry bit using the ADC instruction. Thus, after adding each data item we add with carry the immediate operand 00 into Accumulator B. This has the effect of adding one to the high byte of the result if the carry bit is set, or zero if it is clear, as required.

We also need to keep account of the number of items added so that we can stop the process when they have all been dealt with. In this program the number of items is loaded into location 06 initially and this location is decremented after each addition, stopping when the contents fall to zero. The program finally stores the low byte of the sum (built up in Accumulator A) into location 09 and the high byte (built up in Accumulator B) into 08.

In this program the data is assumed to be loaded into locations 50 to 5F (hex), and the number of items in location 06. The index register is loaded with the starting address of the block of data, 0050. The microprocessor is the 6800.

| *Instruction* | *Code* | *Comment* |
|---|---|---|
| CLR A | 4F | Clear Acc. A |
| CLR B | 5F | Clear Acc. B |
| LDX #0050 | CE 00 50 | Load IR with starting address |
| LOOP:  ADD A 00,X | AB 00 | Add next data item |
| ADC B #00 | C9 00 | Add carry into Acc. B |
| INX | 08 | Increment IR |
| DEC 08 | 6A 00 08 | Decrement item count |
| BNE LOOP | 26 F6 | Branch back to LOOP if not finished |
| STA A 09 | 97 09 | Store low byte of sum |
| STA B 08 | D7 08 | Store high byte of sum |

An alternative way of terminating the loop would be to compare the value in the index register with the last data address, 005F. This allows us to dispense with the decrementing of location 08, and since CPX needs only three clock cycles compared with six cycles for DEC 08 the program will run more quickly.

The CPX #005F instruction would replace DEC 08, and all other instructions could remain unaltered.

As the 6800 has only 8-bit arithmetic, special arrangements are needed to cope with the carry. This can be avoided with the Z80 as 16-bit addition can be used. In the following program the sum is accumulated in the HL register pair. By clearing register D and loading each data item into E, the pair DE can be added to HL, and the 16-bit arithmetic automatically takes care of any carry from L to H. The loop is most easily controlled by using register B as a counter. This has an associated instruction DJNZ (Decrement and Jump if Non Zero) which decrements the counter and jumps back to the beginning of the loop if the counter has not reached zero. In this program for the Z80 the number of items is held in location 1000, the sum is loaded into 1001 and 1002, and the data is in locations 1010 to 101F.

|  | Instruction | Code | Comment |
|---|---|---|---|
|  | XOR A | AF | Clear carry bit and Acc. |
|  | LD D,A | 57 | Clear D |
|  | LD H,A | 67 | Clear H |
|  | LD L,A | 6F | Clear L |
|  | LD A, (1000) | 3A 00 10 | Fetch number of items |
|  | LD B, A | 47 | Load into B |
|  | LD IX, #1010 | DD 21 10 10 | Put address of first number into index register IX |
| LOOP: | LD E, (IX+00) | DD 5E 00 | Fetch next number |
|  | ADD HL,DE | 19 | Add into running total |
|  | INC IX | DD 23 | Increment Index Register |
|  | DJNZ LOOP | 10 F8 | Decrement B and jump if non-zero |
|  | LD (1001), HL | 22 01 10 | Store sum in 1001/2 |

In this program we cannot load register B directly from an external address unless it is first entered into HL. It is thus simpler to load A from location 1000 and then transfer the data to B. Note that no register is specified in the DJNZ LOOP instruction since this works only on the B register, and its use is assumed.

If this program is run with 10 in location 1000 and data items 50, 51, 52, . . . 5F in locations 1010 to 101F, the result is 78 in location 1001 and 05 in 1002. The sum of the numbers is thus 0578, since the low byte is stored first.

Somewhat more house-keeping is needed when using the 6502 since it has only one accumulator and no general-purpose registers. One strategy is to store the low byte of the running total in the accumulator and increment a location in the external store each time the carry bit is set. The data is accessed as in the other programs by using the index register. Since this holds only 8 bits it is initially cleared and the displacement held in the ADC instruction is made equal to the address 1050 of the first data item. The 6502 has a form of indexed addressing in which a two-byte displacement can be incorporated into the instruction; this is just what we need here. The addition loop is ended by comparing the contents of the index register with 10 and leaving the loop when equality is reached. Since the program increments and then tests the IR after having added an item to the running total, the IR will contain 0F when the last item has been added. This will be incremented to 10 and the program will then leave the loop and store the low byte of the sum in location 1001.

A program for the 6502 using this strategy is

| | *Instruction* | *Code* | *Comment* |
|---|---|---|---|
| | LDA #00 | A9 00 | Clear Accumulator |
| | TAX | AA | Clear Index Register IX |
| | STA 1002 | 8D 02 10 | Clear 1002 for high byte |
| | CLC | 18 | Clear carry bit |
| LOOP: | ADC 1050,X | 7D 50 10 | Add next number |
| | BCC NEXT | 90 04 | Branch if carry clear |
| | INC 1002 | EE 02 10 | Increment high byte |
| NEXT: | INX | E8 | Increment IX |
| | CPX #10 | E0 10 | Compare IX with 10 |
| | BNE LOOP | D0 F3 | Branch back to LOOP if unequal |
| | STA 1001 | 8D 01 10 | Store low byte in 1001 |

This program is not as general as it could be, since each time we change the number of items to be added we need to change the immediate operand in the CPX #10 instruction. This can be avoided by storing one more than the number of items (here 10 hex) in, say, location 1000. The compare instruction then becomes CPX 1000 using absolute addressing. The program would then operate with any number of items, the only restriction being that their total should not exceed FFFF hex, as there is provision only for a 16-bit sum. The preliminary set-up procedure requires only the entry of the data, starting at location 1050, and the number of items plus 1 into location 1000.

We next consider the task of multiplication, which can also be effected by the process of repeated addition used above. The loop can, however, be shorter since we use the same quantity to add in each time.

## 5.6 Multiplication

The simplest method of generating the product of two numbers is by repeated addition. Thus, to multiply 5 by 3 we start with a cleared register and add 5 into it 3 times. This leads to a compact program, but one which may be slow to execute since multiplying two 8-bit numbers may involve up to 255 (decimal) additions. However, if time allows, it has the advantage of needing the smallest amount of program storage.

An important point in the design of any multiplication program is that the product of two 8-bit numbers may contain up to 16 bits. Thus we must make provision for a double-length product if there is no restriction on the size of the numbers. The 6800 is a convenient microprocessor to use as the two accumulators can be used to hold the running total. In the following program, accumulator A stores the high byte and accumulator B the low byte of the product. The two numbers are in locations 0010 and 0011 and the product is loaded into 0012 (high byte) and 0013 (low byte). The number in location 0011 is decremented down to zero in the course of the program, and is thus destroyed. If, as is usual, the program is written as a subroutine, this may not matter as new data would be entered each time the program was executed. Otherwise a copy of the contents of 0011 should be loaded into a temporary store and this, not 0011, should be decremented.

The program for multiplication by repeated addition using the 6800 is

| | Instruction | Code | Comment |
|---|---|---|---|
| | CLR A | 4F | Clear Acc. A for high byte |
| | CLR B | 5F | Clear Acc. B for low byte |
| LOOP: | ADD B 10 | DB 10 | Add first number to B |
| | ADC A #00 | 89 00 | Add carry to A |
| | DEC 0011 | 7A 00 11 | Decrement second number |
| | BNE LOOP | 26 F7 | Repeat if not zero |
| | STA A 12 | 97 12 | Store high byte of product |
| | STA B 13 | D7 13 | Store low byte of product |

If the numbers are 12 and 34 the product will be 03A8 (all hex).

This program gives the correct result only when the two numbers are treated as unsigned, that is in the range 0 to FF hex or 0 to 255 decimal. Its answers are incorrect if either number is negative and encoded in two's complement notation.

A longer program is needed for the 'shift and add' method, but this executes more quickly as the loop need be traversed only 8 times. The process resembles long multiplication, but as we are using binary notation we need only multiply by either 0 or 1. This means that we inspect each digit of the multiplier in turn, starting with the least significant; if this is 0 we do nothing, if it is 1 we add in the multiplicand. The running total is then shifted right and the next digit of the multiplicand is inspected. This is done by rotating the accumulator holding it right, which puts the digit concerned into the carry bit. As each bit of the multiplier has been examined it is discarded and as the multiplier moves to the right it makes way for the running total.

We start with the multiplier in accumulator B and accumulator A cleared. At the end the multiplier has been shifted out, accumulator B holds the low byte of the product and accumulator A the high byte. These are finally loaded into locations 12 (high byte) and 13 (low byte). The multiplier and multiplicand are initially loaded into 10 and 11, and 14 is used as a counter. The program loads 8 into location 14 and decrements it each time the loop is executed, stopping when it reaches 0. The program can be shortened a little by dispensing with the counter and testing accumulator B after each shift. If the contents are 0 we leave the loop. This scheme will give a shorter execution time if there are any 0s on the left-hand end of the multiplier. Thus, with 01100101 as a multiplier the loop will be executed only 7 times, stopping when the most significant 1 has been shifted out. The program for a 6800 is

| | Instruction | Code | Comment |
|---|---|---|---|
| | LDA A #08 | 86 08 | Load 8 into Acc. A |
| | STA A 14 | 97 13 | Store in Loc. 14 for counter |
| | LDA B 11 | D6 11 | Load multiplier into Acc. B |
| | CLR A | 4F | Clear Acc. A for product |
| | ROR B | 56 | Fetch LSB of multiplier |
| LOOP: | BCC SHIFT | 24 03 | Branch if carry is clear |
| | · ADD A 10 | 9B 10 | Carry set, add multiplicand |
| SHIFT: | ROR A | 46 | Rotate Acc. A right |
| | ROR B | 56 | Rotate Acc. B right |
| | DEC 14 | 7A 00 14 | Decrement counter |
| | BNE LOOP | 26 F4 | Repeat if counter not zero |
| | STA A 12 | 97 12 | Store product (high byte) |
| | STA B 13 | D7 13 | Store product (low byte) |

The ROR A instruction puts the LSB of the running total into the carry bit; the following ROR B takes this carry bit and loads it into the MSB of accumulator B. The result is a right shift of the two accumulators, considered as a single 16-bit register.

One problem with this program is that it does not give the correct result with negative numbers; if we need to handle these the program can be preceded by a test for the sign of the numbers, any negative number being negated. If this is done once, the product must also be negated. If it is done twice or not at all, the produce is correct. In order to negate the 16-bit product we must negate the low byte and complement the high byte.

With the Z80 we can use 16-bit arithmetic and so in a repeated addition program we do not need to worry about handling the carry which occurs when we have only 8-bit registers. The following program uses the HL register pair to accumulate the product. Register D is cleared and the multiplicand is loaded into E. We then add DE to HL, a 16-bit operation. The multiplier is loaded into B so that we can control the loop with the DJNZ instruction. This program holds the two numbers, NUM1 and NUM2, in locations 1000 and 1001 and puts their product into locations 1002 and 1003.

| Instruction | Code | Comment |
|---|---|---|
| LD HL, #1000 | 21 00 10 | Load address of NUM1 into HL |
| LD B, (HL) | 46 | Load NUM1 into Reg. B |
| INC HL | 23 | Increment data pointer |
| LD E, (HL) | 5E | Load NUM2 into Reg. E |
| XOR A | AF | Clear A |
| LD D, A | 57 | Clear D |
| LD H, A | 67 | Clear H |
| LD L, A | 6F | Clear L |
| LOOP:   ADD HL, DE | 19 | Add NUM2 to HL |
| DJNZ LOOP | 10 FD | Decrement B, repeat if not zero |
| LD (1002), HL | 22 02 10 | Load product into 1002 and 1003 |

This program takes 16 bytes of storage compared with 15 bytes for the 6800 program. However it can handle data loaded anywhere in the address space, whereas the 6800 program only handles data in page zero. If the 6800 is also required to handle data loaded anywhere, extended addressing must be used and the program will occupy 18 bytes.

A multiplication program for the 6502 using repeated addition is similar to that for the 6800, but as we have only one accumulator a storage location must be used to hold the high byte of the product rather than the second accumulator. In the following program the two numbers are stored in locations 10 and 11 and the product is loaded into 12 and 13.

| Instruction | Code | Comment |
|---|---|---|
| LDA #00 | A9 00 | Clear Accumulator |
| STA 13 | 85 13 | Clear 13 for high byte of product |
| LOOP:   CLC | 18 | Clear carry bit |
| ADC NUM1 | 65 10 | Add NUM1 to running total |
| BCC DOWN | 90 02 | Skip next instr. if carry is clear |
| INC 13 | E6 13 | Increment high byte of product |
| DOWN:   DEC NUM2 | C6 11 | Decrement multiplier |
| BNE LOOP | D0 F6 | Repeat if NUM2 not zero |
| STA 12 | 85 12 | Store low byte of product in 12 |

Having only one accumulator, the 6502 needs 17 bytes for this program compared with the 15 bytes needed for the corresponding program using a 6800.

For completeness, we should include the use of left shifts to multiply numbers. These of course only provide directly for a multiplier of 2, 4, 8, 16, etc. However, it may sometimes be quicker to use this scheme than to use repeated addition. For example, it is quicker to multiply by 10 using the following steps. We start with the number X, say.

1. Left shift gives   2X
2. Put in temporary store (usually on the stack)
3. Left shift twice gives   8X
4. Add 2X from temporary store gives   10X

This process is needed when converting from decimal notation to binary. A program which converts a two-digit number in BCD code into binary is given in section 5.8.

## 5.7   Division

The simplest division program is similar to the repeated addition program for multiplication, but uses repeated subtraction. The divisor is subtracted from the dividend as many times as possible, the number of subtractions being equal to the quotient. The criterion for ending the process is that the remainder should be less than the divisor. Usually it is simpler to continue subtraction until the remainder becomes negative; we know then that we have performed one subtraction too many and we add the divisor back to give a positive remainder and subtract one from the previous quotient. This last step gives the process its name of 'restoring division'. The following program for the 6800 handles an 8-bit dividend and an 8-bit divisor. The dividend and divisor, both assumed positive, are held in locations 10 and 11, and the quotient and remainder are put into 13 and 14.

| | Instruction | Code | Comment |
|---|---|---|---|
| | CLR A | 4F | Clear Acc. for quotient |
| | LDA B 10 | D6 10 | Load dividend into Acc. B |
| LOOP: | INC A | 4C | Increment quotient |
| | SUB B 11 | D0 11 | Subtract divisor from B |
| | BGE LOOP | 2C FB | Repeat if result positive |
| | ADD B 11 | DB 11 | Result negative, add divisor |
| | DEC A | 4A | Decrement quotient |
| | STA A 12 | 97 12 | Store quotient in 12 |
| | STA B 13 | D7 13 | Store remainder in 13 |

The program subtracts the divisor from the dividend in the loop; the ADD B 11 and DEC A instructions restore the remainder and quotient when the loop has been terminated by a negative value for the remainder.

As the Z80 has facilities for 16-bit arithmetic, a similar program which handles a 16-bit dividend and an 8-bit divisor needs little more program space. The following program holds the dividend in locations 1000 and 1001, the divisor in 1002, and loads the quotient and the remainder into 1003 and 1004.

| Instruction | Code | Comment |
|---|---|---|
| XOR A | AF | Clear A |
| LD D, A | 57 | Clear D |
| LD B, A | 47 | Clear B for quotient |
| LD HL, (1000) | 2A 00 10 | Load dividend into HL |
| LD A, (1002) | 3A 02 10 | Fetch divisor |
| LD E, A | 5F | Load into E |
| LOOP:  INC B | 04 | Increment quotient |
| SBC HL, DE | ED 52 | Subtract divisor from dividend |
| JR NC, LOOP | 30 FB | Repeat if result positive |
| ADD HL, DE | 19 | Result neg. restore remainder |
| DEC B | 05 | Restore quotient |
| LD A, L | 7D | Fetch remainder |
| LD (1003), A | 32 03 10 | Load it into 1003 |
| LD A, B | 78 | Fetch quotient |
| LD (1004), A | 32 04 10 | Load it into 1004 |

Note that we do not need to clear the carry bit before the SBC HL, DE instruction since the initial XOR does this, and none of the intervening instructions will affect the carry bit.

As the test for the end of the loop is the setting of the carry bit after the SBC HL,DE instruction, the program will work only with positive numbers. As with the multiply program we can produce an alternative program which simulates manual long division. This will occupy more store space than the program above but will execute more quickly.

### 5.8  Decimal-to-Binary Conversion

When data is collected from a manual keyboard, or from some instruments such as digital voltmeters, it is most likely to be encoded in BCD format. Unless we need only perform relatively trivial arithmetic on it, the next task will be to convert the data into binary form. The following program for a Z80 converts a two-digit BCD number held in location 1000 into an 8-bit binary number which is loaded into 1001. The ten's digit occupies the four MS bits in location 1000 and the unit's digit the four LS bits. The algorithm is

(1)    Copy BCD No. onto stack
(2)    Mask out unit's digit
(3)    Shift No. right, giving 8 times ten's digit T
(4)    Copy this onto stack
(5)    Shift No. right twice, giving 2T
(6)    Copy into Reg. C
(7)    Fetch 8T from stack

(8)   Add 2T, giving 10T in all
(9)   Copy into C
(10)  Fetch BCD No. from stack
(11)  Mask out ten's digit
(12)  Add to 10T, giving 10T + U as required
(13)  Store result in 1001

Here T denotes the ten's digit and U the unit's digit, and the result in 1001 is 10T + U. We can use this program as a subroutine when converting longer numbers by using nested multiplication. Thus a three-digit BCD number H T U whose value is 100H + 10T + U can be written as 10(10H+T)+U. Two calls to the sub-routine with the appropriate data will then convert the number to binary. However, unless we restrict the input data to less than 256 (decimal) the program will need minor changes since we will no longer be able to store the result in a single byte.
The program is

| Instruction | Code | Comment |
|---|---|---|
| LD A, (1000) | 3A 00 10 | Fetch BCD number |
| PUSH AF | 85 | Put copy on stack |
| LD B # F0 | 06 F0 | Load mask into Reg. B |
| AND B | A0 | AND with Acc., masking out units |
| SLR A | CB 3F | Shift right, giving 8T |
| PUSH AF | F5 | Put copy onto stack |
| SLR A | CB 3F | Shift Acc. right, giving 2T |
| LD C, A | 4F | Copy into C |
| POP AF | F1 | Fetch 8T |
| ADD A, C | 81 | Add 2T, giving 10T |
| LD C, A | 4F | Copy into C |
| POP AF | F1 | Fetch BCD number |
| LD B, #0F | 06 0F | Load mask into B |
| AND B | A0 | Mask out ten's digit |
| ADD A, C | 81 | Add 10T, giving 10T + U |
| LD (1001), A | 32 01 10 | Store result in 1001 |

The programs described in this chapter deal with data which has already been loaded into the microprocessor's store. No consideration has been given to the mechanism by which the data could have been collected from external sources, or the methods which could be used to force the microprocessor to attend to requests for service by external devices. In the following chapter we examine the way in which the microprocessor can be made to interrupt its current program and begin execution of another program which services some device connected to it.

# 6 *Program Interrupts*

## 6.1 Timing Data Transfers

Nearly all microprocessors are components in some larger system which has to collect data from the outside world and send information to it. The microprocessor has its own internal clock which provides the timing signals needed for the execution of its program, and which is independent of any external events. If we consider the input of data, we need to synchronise two events: the arrival of the data at the microprocessor interface, and the execution of the instruction which reads it into the system.

Three methods of solving the timing problem are

(1) Program-controlled transfers,
(2) Interrupt driven transfers, and
(3) Direct memory access (DMA)

In program-controlled transfers the data movements occur when the program reaches an input or output statement. These transfer a byte of data via the data bus and the device interface to or from an external device. One of the problems which arises in this scheme is that of synchronising the data flow at the interface with the execution of the input or output instruction. This is more acute with a high data rate; the data must be transferred quickly, otherwise the next byte will arrive before the current one has been dealt with, so causing errors. One way of tackling the problem is to provide facilities for signalling between the microprocessor and the device, usually by a single bit store called a *flag*. Considering the input of data, the usual arrangement would be to enable the device to set the flag as soon as the data became available. In addition to collecting data the microprocessor must have facilities for testing the state of the flag. The interface, including flags and other features, is generally provided by a special input/output package which forms part of the family of microprocessor support chips.

This procedure is satisfactory if the program arrives at the flag-testing instruction before the data is ready; a waiting loop will be entered and will be executed until the data arrives and the flag is set. However, if the data arrives first the procedure will fail if it disappears before the program reaches the flag test. Some input/output packages reduce the chance of losing data by having storage of the input data. The data is presented to the package and a strobe pulse from the data source then latches the data in. It remains stored until a further byte and its accompanying strobe pulse replace it. In this arrangement the program must read one byte from the input/output package before the next byte arrives.

Although this procedure is simple and requires a minimum of hardware, it has some disadvantages. The major one is the processor time that may be wasted while the program waits for data, since while the waiting loop is being executed the microprocessor cannot undertake any other calculations. Also, if several devices are attached to the microprocessor the order in which they are accessed is built into the program and cannot be altered while the program is running, so making the scheme rather inflexible.

The general layout of the program is as follows

(1)   Loop:   Test Flag
(2)            Jump back to Loop if Flag is not set
(3)            Flag set, Transfer Data

Many of the disadvantages of program-controlled transfers can be avoided by using program interrupts.

## 6.2   Program Interrupts

The general principle of data transfers controlled by program interrupts is that any device requiring service can interrupt the execution of the main program and transfer the computer's attention to another program (the interrupt service program) which attends to the device. This service program is written like a subroutine, separate from the main program, but the last instruction is Return from Interrupt, not Return from Subroutine. Having the service program separate from the main program enables it to be written and tested independently, so easing the production of the software. It also has the advantage that any changes to the device should require only changes in the service program, not the main program. This makes the task of program maintenance and expansion much simpler.

Although the service program looks much like a subroutine, there are important differences. Firstly, it is called into action not by a Jump to Subroutine instruction, but by an electrical signal from the device. Secondly, it may be invoked at any point in the main program. Thus the main program cannot include any instructions to save the contents of registers before embarking on the service program since we have no means of knowing where to put them. Consequently all saving of registers must occur after the interrupt signal has been accepted and the microprocessor has started its interrupt handling process.

One similarity between a subroutine and an interrupt service program is the need for a return link to the main program; this is provided in both cases by pushing the current contents of the program counter onto the stack before starting to execute the program, and returning them to the program counter immediately before jumping back to the main program.

The 6800, Z80 and 6502 microprocessors all have two interrupt pins labelled INT or IRQ and NMI. The NMI (Non-Maskable Interrupt) pin is always attended to, but the INT or IRQ pin is termed 'maskable'. This means that we can determine by program whether the microprocessor will attend to signals on this line or not. Normally the line is disabled when power is first applied, and after initial operations, such as loading control registers in the peripheral packages, an instruction is included which enables the interrupt line. If it is necessary to conclude some program segments without interruption, the line can be disabled by another instruction. Typical instructions are

| *Microprocessor* | *Enable Interrupts* | *Disable Interrupts* |
|---|---|---|
| 6800 | CLI  Clear Interrupt Mask | SEI  Set Interrupt Mask |
| Z80 | EI    Enable Interrupts | DI    Disable Interrupts |
| 6502 | CLI  Clear Interrupt Mask | SEI  Set Interrupt Mask |

In addition to these overall controls of the interrupt line, the input/output packages enable the interrupt request signals from each device to be individually enabled or disabled, before being passed on to the microprocessor. This is effected by setting or clearing a bit in the package control register.

### 6.3    M6800 Interrupts

If the IRQ line has been enabled by a CLI instruction, the processor will accept an interrupt signalled by an earth on the IRQ pin. The processor first finishes executing the current instruction, and then embarks on the following sequence:

(1)  Load onto the stack the PC, IR, ACC A, ACC B and CCR.
(2)  Set interrupt mask bit to inhibit further interrupts.
(3)  Copy FFF8 into PCH and FFF9 into PCL.
(4)  Fetch next instruction (the first in the interrupt service routine) from the address loaded into the PC.

Here PCL and PCH denote the low and high bytes of the PC.

This scheme allows the service program to be loaded anywhere in the address space, but the address of the first instruction in it must be loaded into FFF8 (high byte) and FFF9 (low byte). The hardware of the 6800 always reads FFF8 and FFF9 to find the location of the interrupt service routine. Although this process is simple if only a few devices are allowed to create interrupts, it will be slow if there are many. This is because the microprocessor provides no mechanism for determining quickly which of the devices has requested service, since they are all connected to the same IRQ line. Thus the first part of the service routine must consist of a sequence of instructions which test the state of every flag which indicates a program interrupt request.

Each test instruction must be linked to a jump instruction so that as soon as a flag which is set has been found, the microprocessor jumps to the service program for that device which set the flag. One advantage of the 6800 is that the program need not worry about saving the contents of the processor registers; this is done automatically during the interrupt handling process. Since the PC and IR are both 16-bit registers, seven bytes in all are pushed onto the stack. A single RTI instruction at the end of the service program will pull these seven bytes off the stack and return them to the processor registers.

The program below is a simple service routine which counts the number of 1s in a byte held in location 00 and loads the result into 01. It is part of an alarm-monitoring process in which each bit in 00 represents the signal on one alarm line and the number of active lines indicates the severity of the event. Each bit is moved in turn into the carry bit, and added into Acc. B. After each addition the remaining number is tested and if it contains no more 1s the process is ended and the result loaded into location 01. The logical shift is used so that a zero is entered into the MS bit of Acc. A as the LS bit is moved into the carry bit.

| | Instruction | Code | Comment |
|---|---|---|---|
| | CLR B | 5F | Clear Acc. B for result |
| | LDA A 00 | 96 00 | Fetch number from 00 |
| LOOP: | LSR A | 44 | Shift LS bit into Carry bit |
| | ADC B #00 | C9 00 | Add Carry into Acc. B |
| | TST A | 4D | Test Acc. A |
| | BEQ OUT | 27 02 | Finish if no more 1s |
| | BRA LOOP | 20 F8 | Otherwise repeat |
| OUT: | STA B 01 | D7 01 | Store result in 01 |
| | CLI | 0E | Enable interrupts |
| | RTI | 3B | Return from interrupt |

## 6.4 Interrupt Recognition

If more than one device can request program interrupts the first part of the service routine must scan the interrupt flags to determine which device is active, and then jump to the corresponding service routine. If more than one device is active, the microprocessor will attend to the device whose flag is tested first. Consequently the order of the flag tests determines the order in which the devices receive attention. This should correspond with the priority order of the devices. Once this has been written into the program, it cannot be changed while the program is running.

Each of the parallel I/O packages for the 6800, coded 6821, provides two 8-bit ports for external devices. Each port has two flag bits. Flags CA1 and CA2 occupy bits 7 and 6 of control register A (CRA) and are controlled by port A. Flags CB1 and CB2 occupy the corresponding bits of CRB for port B. Thus a flag-testing routine for this package could be as follows.

| *Instruction* | *Code* | *Comment* |
|---|---|---|
| LDA A CRA | B6 80 01 | Fetch copy of CRA |
| BMI SVC1 | 2B XX | Branch to service routine 1 if flag 1 set |
| AND A #40 | 84 40 | Mask out bit 6 |
| BNE SVC2 | 26 XX | Branch to service routine 2 if flag 2 set |
| LDA A CRB | B6 8003 | Fetch copy of CRB |
| BMI SVC3 | 2B XX | Branch to service routine 3 if flag 3 set |
| AND A #40 | 84 40 | Mask out bit 6 |
| BNE SVC4 | 26 XX | Branch to service routine 4 if flag 4 set |

Here the addresses of CRA and CRB are 8001 and 8003. If bit 7 (flag 1 or 3) is set the contents of CRA or CRB will have the MS bit set, and so when they are loaded into Acc. A the N bit will be set. The condition for the BMI instruction will be satisfied and the program will branch to the service routine. In order to test the other flags held in bit 6 of the control register all other bits must be masked out. Here this is done by an AND instruction with the operand 01000000, so clearing all bits other than bit 6. If this bit is set the condition for the BNE (branch if not equal to zero) instruction is satisfied and the program branches to the service routine. The displacements represented by the letters XX depend upon the addresses of the service routines.

Interrupts using the NMI line are handled in the same way as those which use the IRQ line, with two exceptions:

(1)    The NMI line cannot be disabled, so interrupt requests will always be granted and will take precedence over IRQ requests.
(2)    The address of the first byte of the service program must be loaded into locations FFFC (high byte) and FFFD (low byte).

The NMI line is normally reserved for the highest priority interrupt.

The address of the service routine is sometimes called the 'interrupt vector', and the process of directing the computer to the interrupt service routine called 'vectoring'. The software vectoring scheme described above needs a minimum of hardware, but the time which elapses between the signal on the IRQ line and the start of the service routine may become too large if many devices are connected. One solution to this problem is to use hardware vectoring; in the 6800 this requires a special priority interrupt package which accepts eight interrupt request lines and detects the active line having the highest priority. Its identity is signalled to a small read only store which holds all of the interrupt vectors. When the addresses FFF8 and FFF9 appear on the address bus, the interrupt vector corresponding to the highest priority device which is requesting service is read from the store and sent to the data bus. The microprocessor then starts executing the service routine, having obtained its address from the store rather than locations FFF8 and FFF9.

At the cost of extra hardware the flag-testing sequence can be omitted and the only interrupt service program needed is a set of routines which service the individual devices connected to the priority interrupt package.

## 6.5   Z80 Interrupts

Like the 6800 the Z80 has both maskable and non-maskable interrupt lines ($\overline{\text{INT}}$ and $\overline{\text{NMI}}$), but the $\overline{\text{INT}}$ line has a facility for some hardware vectoring. Three interrupt modes are available:

*Mode 0*. This is identical to the 8080 interrupt mode and is the mode entered when resetting the microprocessor after power is applied. The Z80 expects the instruction following the interrupt to be supplied by the interrupting device rather than the program store. Normally this is an RST N (Restart) instruction which causes a jump to location N, where N has one of the 8 values 00, 08, 18, . . . 38 (hex).

The binary format of the Restart instruction is 11XXX111, where XXX has one of the values 000 to 111. Thus RST 18 is 11011111 in binary. The format is chosen to minimise the hardware needed to generate the Restart instruction. The data lines normally have resistors which pull their potential to the logic 1 level when no device is driving them. Thus to generate the RST 18 instruction we need only a single driver connected to Data line D5 which will pull its potential down to earth when an interrupt is accepted.

This scheme allows up to eight devices to be directly vectored so that a few microseconds after a device has sent an interrupt request, the corresponding interrupt service routine will start to be executed. This only happens for all devices if no other device is requesting service at the same time. Just as with the software flag-testing routine, the devices must have a priority order assigned to them; in this case it is determined by the order in which they are connected to the Interrupt Acknowledge signal. This is connected through each interface and when any device requests an interrupt, it prevents the signal travelling further down the line. In consequence, when more than one device calls, only that nearest to the processor will receive the signal and will send its RST N instruction onto the data bus. This arrangement prevents two or more interfaces trying to drive the data bus at the same time.

The Z80 interrupt service program thus needs no flag-testing segment if no more than eight devices are permitted to create interrupts. It will consist of a number of separate modules, starting at locations 00, 08, 10, etc. Unless these are very short, the first instruction will be a jump to an area higher in the storage space where there is room for the program, since the set of starting addresses built into the microprocessor are spaced only 8 bytes apart.

*Mode 1* interrupts use a single address, 0038, to which the microprocessor jumps when the interrupt is accepted. This scheme is intended for simple systems where only one device or two devices can request interrupts. It is simpler to use than Mode 0 since the device need not send an RST N instruction to provide an interrupt vector.

*Mode 2* interrupts are the most powerful and enable up to 128 devices to direct the microprocessor to their own service routines. They have some similarity to Mode 0 in that the device must send a byte of data to the microprocessor to provide a vector address, but instead of an RST N instruction the data is the lower byte of a 16-bit address XXXX. This holds the low byte and the next byte holds the high byte of the address of the start of the service routine. The high byte of XXXX is obtained from the I register in the processor. This is an 8-bit register which can be loaded via the Accumulator. The only operations which can be performed on it are to load it from the accumulator, or to load the accumulator from it. As with Mode 0 the interrupt acknowledge signal is sent through all devices which can create interrupts so that if several devices request service, only that which is nearest to the microprocessor will receive attention. This connection is usually called a 'daisy-chain'.

As an example, if the I register contains 30, and the device puts the number 46 onto the data bus, the microprocessor assembles these into the 16-bit address 3046. If this holds 20 and the next byte, 3047, holds 10, the microprocessor will read these two and form the address 1020. It will finally fetch the first byte of the interrupt service from location 1020. The block of storage from 3000 to 30FF will contain the pointers to the service routines which can be located anywhere in the storage space.

The interrupt mode can be set by program using the following instructions.

|        | *Instruction* | *Code* |
|--------|---------------|--------|
| Mode 0 | IM0           | ED 46  |
| Mode 1 | IM1           | ED 56  |
| Mode 2 | IM2           | ED 5E  |

### 6.6    Z80 Interrupt Service Routines

Z80 service routines differ from those written for the 6800 because there is no automatic saving of processor registers. Thus if any of the A, F, B, C, D, E, H or L registers is used in the service routine, its previous contents must first of all be saved by the program and must be restored just before returning to the main program. This can be done using the stack, but a faster mechanism has been provided by the designers of the Z80. Each of the eight registers named above has a duplicate register with which its contents can be exchanged. Two instructions are available for this, EX AF, AF' (Code 08) which exchanges the accumulator and the flag register, and EXX' (Code D9) which exchanges the BC DE and HL registers. The routine must end with two instructions which enable the interrupts and return to the main program. Thus for a maskable interrupt the structure of the service program will be

| *Instruction* | *Comment* |
|---|---|
| EX AF, AF' | Save accumulator and flag registers |
| EXX' | Save remaining registers |
| . . . | |
| Body of routine | |
| . . . | |
| EX AF, AF' | Restore accumulator and flags |
| EXX' | Restore remaining registers |
| EI | Enable interrupts |
| RTI | Return from interrupt |

This assumes that the routine will use the accumulator and at least one of the other registers. A similar scheme is suitable for the non-maskable interrupt $\overline{\text{NMI}}$, but as this cannot be disabled the EI instruction is not needed, and the last instruction should be RTN.

## 6.7   6502 Interrupts

The 6502 has two interrupt pins, $\overline{\text{IRQ}}$ and $\overline{\text{NMI}}$, which operate in the same way as those of the 6800, but using different vector locations. The $\overline{\text{IRQ}}$ pin is maskable and when it is active the microprocessor reads two bytes from locations FFFE and FFFF. These are assembled as a 16-bit address from which the first instruction of the service routine is fetched. The NMI interrupt acts similarly but uses the locations FFFA and FFFB. As with the 6800, if more than one device can create an interrupt the first part of the service routine must be a flag-testing sequence to identify the highest-priority device requesting service.

One of the peripheral packages for parallel data transfers, the 6520 PIA, resembles closely the 6821 package used with the 6800. In particular, it has the same control register configuration, so that the same flag-testing program can be used. If all of the control lines are used as inputs, the program must test bit 6 and bit 7 of each control register. In the following routine the control registers are addressed at A0001 (A side) and A003 (B side).

| Instruction | Code | Comment |
|---|---|---|
| LDA CRA | AD 01 A0 | Fetch copy of CRA |
| BMI SV1 | 30 XX | Branch to service routine 1 if flag 1 set |
| AND #40 | 29 40 | Mask out bit 6 |
| BNE SV2 | D0 XX | Branch to service routine 2 if flag 2 set |
| LDA CRB | AD 03 A0 | Fetch copy of CRB |
| BMI SV3 | 30 XX | Branch to service routine 3 if flag 3 set |
| AND #40 | 29 40 | Mask out bit 6 |
| BNE SV4 | D0 XX | Branch to service routine 4 if flag 4 set |

The offsets XX depend on the position of the service routines relative to the branch instructions. As with the 6800, the $\overline{\text{IRQ}}$ line is initially disabled by the reset signal when power is first applied, and is also disabled when an $\overline{\text{IRQ}}$ interrupt is accepted. Usually the $\overline{\text{IRQ}}$ line is enabled at the end of the service routine, just before the return to the main program.

Although a device may be allowed to drive the IRQ line directly, much more flexibility is provided, and also storage, if the device drives one of the control lines of a PIA. We consider the programming and use of these packages in the following chapter.

## 6.8   DMA Transfers

Most microprocessors have to respond to events in the outside world which occur at random intervals of time. Although program interrupts enable us to deal with most of these events, they cannot always provide a fast enough data rate, since each event requires the processor to execute a number of instructions. For example, if we are sampling a voltage waveform at regular intervals and reading the value of each sample into the microprocessor store for subsequent analysis, the following operations will be needed after taking each sample and converting the voltage into a digital value:

(1) Transfer data from the converter to the accumulator.
(2) Transfer data from the accumulator to the store.
(3) Increment the store address.
(4) Decrement the data counter.
(5) Test whether the data counter has reached zero.

This assumes that we have allocated a block of storage to hold the data and that the data counter is initially loaded with the number of bytes which are to be transferred. Using a 6800 processor with a 1 MHz clock rate, these operations may take about 20 microseconds, plus about 13 microseconds for moving control from the main program to the service routine. This is the most favourable situation with no other device competing for interrupts and so no time is spent in an interrupt recognition program. Thus the sampling rate is limited to about 3000 samples per second.

The only way to handle a faster data rate is to use a transfer process which involves hardware only, called *autonomous transfer* or *Direct Memory Access* (DMA). In this scheme the microprocessor is bypassed and its action is halted while the external device transfers data directly to the store. Transfers can thus occur at the maximum rate at which the store can accept data – in the above case one byte every microsecond. In microprocessor systems the extra hardware is usually provided in a special DMA chip, which contains the following components:

(1) A register which holds the address of the next data byte to be transferred. This is automatically incremented after each transfer and must initially be loaded with the address of the first storage location assigned to hold the data.
(2) A byte counter which is automatically decremented after each byte has been transferred. It must initially be loaded with the number of bytes of data to be transferred.
(3) A zero-detecting gate attached to the byte counter, which produces an output when the contents of the counter fall to zero. This is usually arranged to create an interrupt which disables further DMA transfers and branches to a program which processes the data gathered.
(4) An output connected to the processor which halts processor operation while DMA transfers are in progress. This must also turn off the line drivers in the processor which feed the data and address buses. In the input action that we have taken as an example, the data lines are driven by the sampling converter and the address lines by the DMA chip. For an output action the data lines would be driven by the storage chip supplying the data.

In order to ensure that no instructions are corrupted, the DMA chip requests a DMA transfer from the processor when the external device produces data. This request is normally granted when the processor has finished executing the current instruction. Two basic transfer modes are used – cycle-stealing and burst mode. Cycle-stealing is used when the external device cannot produce data as fast as the store can absorb it. As each byte of data arrives, a single-byte DMA transfer is requested and control is then returned to the main program. Burst mode is used when a block of data is available. Bytes are transferred in a continuous stream under the control of the DMA interface. This mode is used only with fast data sources or when data is held in a buffer.

The only programming involved in DMA transfers is the initial loading of the address, byte count and control registers. After this, a further transfer to the control register will enable the DMA chip and transfers will occur automatically as each data byte becomes available. We have taken as our example a data write operation. The direction of data flow is determined by a bit in the control register. If the transfer is a read operation from the microprocessor store to some external device, the DMA request will still come from the external device, but it will indicate that the device is ready to receive another byte instead of having a byte ready for the store to accept. Most DMA chips provide four separate data channels, each with its own set of registers, and provide priority adjudication if two or more channels request DMA transfers at the same time.

# 7   *Programming Input/Output*

## 7.1   Input/Output Packages

In order to transfer data between the microprocessor and external devices, hardware is needed to provide temporary storage, to decode some address lines, to communicate with the data bus, to control interrupts, and to synchronise data movement with the processor clock cycles. This can be assembled from small-scale integrated circuits but the package count can be reduced from a dozen or more to one or two by using the special interface packages designed by the microprocessor manufacturer. The most widely used is the parallel interface which generally provides two 8-bit ports and a few signalling lines for connecting to external devices. In order to afford maximum flexibility in a single design, the package is made programmable. This means that before any data can be transferred one or more internal registers must be loaded.

A typical I/O package is the PIA (Parallel Interface Adapter) for the 6800. This has two ports labelled A and B, each port having three registers. For the A port these are

> CRA   Control Register A
> DDRA   Data Direction Register A
> PA   Data Port A

In order to fabricate the PIA in a standard 40-pin package, only two pins can be devoted to addressing; this means that only four addresses can be used. Since there are six registers in all, the Data Direction Register and the Data Port on either side must share one address. The choice between them is made by bit 2 of the Control Register. The Reset pulse which is generated when power is first applied is connected to all PIAs and initially clears all registers. This means that bits 2 of the Control Registers (CRA2 and CRB2) are zero and the Data Direction Register is connected to the data bus. Each bit of the Data Port can be programmed separately as input or output, by making the corresponding bit of the DDR zero or one. Thus initially the ports are set for input, and ones must be written to the DDR for each bit of the Data Port which is required as an output.

As an example, if we need the four high bits (D4 to D7) as outputs and the four low bits as inputs we need to write the bit pattern 11110000 (F0 in hex) to the DDR.

In addition to the eight data lines, each port has two control lines. The first of these (CA1 or CB1) is always an input and the second (CA2 or CB2) can be programmed as either an input or an output. When CA2 is an input the various bits control functions as follows:

| Bit | Function |
|-----|----------|
| CRA0 | Controls CA1 Interrupt, 0 = disable 1 = enable |
| CRA1 | Controls active edge of CA1, = 1 for H to L, = 0 for L to H |
| CRA2 | Controls DDRA/PA switch, = 0 for DDRA, = 1 for PA |
| CRA3 | Controls CA2 Interrupt, 0 = disable 1 = enable |
| CRA4 | Controls active edge of CA2, = 1 for H to L, = 0 for L to H |
| CRA5 | Controls direction of CA2, = 0 for input |
| CRA6 | CA2 Flag (read only) |
| CRA7 | CA1 Flag (read only) |

An active transition on CA1 (CA2) always sets the flag CRA7 (CRA6) but will only request an interrupt on the IRQ line if bit CRA0 (CRA3) is set. The polarity of the active transition is decided by CRA1 (CRA4). The bits in brackets relate to the CA2 line, the others to the CA1 line. The two flags in each port are unusual (and somewhat frustrating), as they are read only. This means that once they have been set by signals on the control lines they can only be cleared by reading the data ports PA and PB. In some circumstances there is no need to read the data, for example when counting the number of times the flag has been set in a given period to determine speed. It is then necessary to perform a 'dummy' read each time the counter is incremented to clear the flag ready for the next count.

When CA2 is needed for output, CRA5 is set to 1. Usually CA2 is used to signal that a byte of data has been sent to the port and is available to the external device, and CRA4 is set to 0. If CRA4 is set to 1, CA2 acts as an extra output line and copies the data loaded into CRA3 by the processor.

The action of bit 2 (CRA2) is shown in figure 7.1 in which the following addresses are assumed:

| | |
|------|---------|
| 8040 | DDRA/PA |
| 8041 | CRA |
| 8042 | DDRB/PB |
| 8043 | CRB |

## 7.2  Programming the 6821

There are two stages in programming the 6821: setting up the control and data registers, and then transferring data. We will assume that PA is to have bits D0 to D3 as outputs and D4 to D7 as inputs; CA1 and CA2 are to be inputs, with CA2

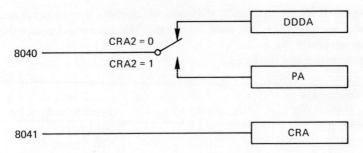

Figure 7.1 Using bit CRA2 to control access to **DDRA** and **PA**.

creating an interrupt and CA1 just setting the flag. Both control lines are active on the negative (high to low) transition. Assuming that power has just been applied, all registers in the PIA will be cleared. Thus a byte sent to location 8040 will load the DDR. We need 1 in the four lower bits for output and 0 in the four higher bits for input, so that the byte needed is 00001111 or 0F in hex. The control register needs the following bit pattern:

|  |  |
|---|---|
| CRA0 = 0 | Disables interrupts on CA1 |
| CRA1 = 0 | CA1 active on negative transition |
| CRA2 = 1 | Next byte sent to 8040 goes to PA |
| CRA3 = 1 | CA2 can create an interrupt |
| CRA4 = 0 | CA2 active on negative transition |
| CRA5 = 0 | CA2 is an input |
| CRA6 = 0 ⎫ | Read only pins, bit written |
| CRA7 = 0 ⎭ | has no effect |

The bit pattern is thus 00001100 or 0C in hex. The program to initialise Port A is thus:

| *Instruction* | *Code* | *Comment* |
|---|---|---|
| LDA A #0F | 86 0F | Load Acc. A with 0F |
| STA A 8040 | B7 80 40 | Copy into DDRA |
| LDA A #0C | 86 0C | Load Acc. A with 0C |
| STA A 8041 | B7 80 41 | Copy into CRA |

We will assume that the four MS bits read a BCD number which is to be loaded into the four LS bits of Acc. B. We shall need to read all eight bits, mask off the four LS bits and then shift the four MS bits four places to the right. Thus if we read 7A or 0111 1010 in binary, the operations needed are

| | | |
|---|---|---|
| Initial read | 0111 1010 | |
| Mask off 4 LS bits | 0111 0000 | (mask is 1111 0000 or F0) |
| Shift 4 places right | 0000 0111 | |

However, if we use the logical shift right which puts a 0 into the MS bit after each shift, we do not need the mask instruction. The shifting will ensure that the four MS bits are 0.

A suitable program would be

| Instruction | Code | Comment |
|---|---|---|
| LDA B 8040 | F6 80 40 | Fetch byte from PA |
| LSR B | 54 | Shift right |
| LSR B | 54 | Shift right |
| LSR B | 54 | Shift right |
| LSR B | 54 | Shift right |

Since CA2 can create interrupts, we will assume that it is connected to a sensor which detects light passing through the slits of an optical disc. The disc is attached to a rotating shaft and is used to measure its speed. Each time a slit passes across the sensor a pulse is generated on CA2 which creates an interrupt. Each interrupt increments a counter stored in location 0005 and the shaft speed is measured by reading the counter at fixed time intervals and then clearing it.

If there are other interrupts, the first part of the interrupt routine must be a flag-testing sequence. The program which deals with CA2 could be

| Instruction | Code | Comment |
|---|---|---|
| INC 00 05 | 7C 05 | Increment speed counter |
| LDA A 8040 | B6 80 40 | Dummy read of PA to clear flag |
| CLI | 0E | Enable interrupts |
| RTI | 38 | Return from interrupt |

The first instruction increments the counter and performs all of the arithmetic needed, but it must be followed by the dummy read in order to clear the flag ready for the next CA2 pulse.

When writing to the four LS bits of PA which have been programmed as outputs we must send a complete byte, but the four MS bits will be ignored as these are programmed as inputs. To output the bit pattern 0110 to the four LS bits we need to load this into an accumulator and then transfer it to the port PA. The four MS bits are set to zero, so that the output byte needed is 0000 0110, or 06 in hex. A suitable program would be

| Instruction | Code | Comment |
|---|---|---|
| LDA A #06 | 86 06 | Load Acc. with 06 |
| STA A 8040 | B7 80 40 | Transfer to PA |

This use of Port A involves splitting it into four input and four output lines. If we wish to use the Port B for eight output lines, we need to change all bits in

Data Direction Register B to 1. The quickest way to do this is to use the complement instruction, in this case

COM 8042 (coded as 73 80 42).

This instruction must be used when bit 2 of Control Register B is zero, at the beginning of the program segment which sets up the PIA registers.

## 7.3 6502 I/O Packages

The 6502 family has two parallel I/O packages, the 6520 and the 6522. The 6520 PIA is virtually identical to the 6821 and is programmed in the same way. The 6522 VIA (Versatile Interface Adapter) is considerably more complex and has many more internal registers, but can cater for a wider range of applications. Externally it resembles the PIA in having two 8-bit Data Ports, two Data Direction Registers, and four control lines. However, it also has two 16-bit timers and an 8-bit shift register for serial data. In order to access and control all of these registers it has four address lines instead of two, and 16 separate addresses which enable the programmer to access directly 16 registers. The Data Port thus does not need to share an address with the Data Direction Register. Since there are more registers, more flags are needed to indicate their condition, and a complete 8-bit Interrupt Flag Register is devoted to them. The bits have the following significance:

| Bit | Event setting bit | | Event clearing bit |
|-----|-------------------|---|---------------------|
| 0 | CA2 transition (if input) | | Read or write PA |
| 1 | CA1 transition | | Read or write PA |
| 2 | Finish 8 shifts | | Read or write Shift Reg. |
| 3 | CB2 transition (if input) | | Read or write PB |
| 4 | CB1 transition | | Read or write PB |
| 5 | Timer 2 finished | | Read T2 counter low byte |
| | | or | Write T2 counter high byte |
| 6 | Timer 1 finished | | Read T1 counter low byte |
| | | or | Write T1 counter high byte |
| 7 | Active interrupt | | Interrupt cleared |

As there are more activities which can create interrupts than in the PIA, another 8-bit Interrupt Enable Register is devoted to their control. The first seven bits determine whether flags are allowed to create interrupts; if a 1 is written to any bit it is selected for action and is altered to the value written into bit 7. Bits 0 to 6 act on the following flags:

| Bit | 6 | 5 | 4 | 3 | 2 | 1 | 0 |
|------|-----|-----|-----|-----|-----|-----|-----|
| Flag | T1 | T2 | CB1 | CB2 | SR | CA1 | CA2 |

Thus to allow only CB2 and CA2 to create interrupts, we need first to clear all other enable bits. This requires a 0 in bit 7 and a 1 for all flags but CB2 and CA2, which is the pattern 01110110 or 76 in hex. To enable CA2 and CB2 we need a 1 in bits 0, 3 and 7. The bit pattern is 10001001 or 89. If the address of the Interrupt Enable Register (IER) is E00E a suitable program would be

| *Instruction* | *Code* | *Comment* |
|---|---|---|
| LDA #76 | A9 76 | Load Acc. with 76 |
| STA E00E | 8D 0E E0 | Move to IER to disable other interrupts |
| LDA #89 | A9 89 | Load Acc. with 89 |
| STA E00E | 8D 0E E0 | Move to IER to enable CA2 and CB2 interrupts |

The four address pins of the VIA are normally connected to the four lowest address lines of the processor (A0 to A3) so that the VIA registers have 16 consecutive addresses. If the lowest is E000 the allocation is as follows:

| | |
|---|---|
| E000 | Port B output register |
| E001 | Port A output register |
| E002 | Port B direction register |
| E003 | Port A direction register |
| E004 | Timer 1 counter low byte |
| E005 | Timer 1 counter high byte |
| E068 | Timer 1 latch low byte |
| E007 | Timer 1 latch high byte |
| E008 | Timer 2 counter low byte |
| E009 | Timer 2 counter high byte |
| E00A | Serial shift register |
| E00B | Auxiliary control register |
| E00C | Peripheral control register |
| E00D | Interrupt flag register |
| E00E | Interrupt enable register |
| E00F | Port A output register (no handshaking) |

Since there are so many registers available the peripheral control register need only determine the actions of the four control lines, and four bits are allocated for each port. Bits 0 to 3 control CA1 and CA2, while bits 4 to 7 control CB1 and CB2. The bits act as follows:

- Bit 0    If 0, active edge of CA1 is 1 to 0, if 1 it is 0 to 1
- Bit 1    When CA2 is an input, = 0 for normal mode, = 1 for independent mode
- Bit 2    If 0 when CA2 is an input, active edge is 1 to 0, if 1 the active edge is 0 to 1
- Bit 3    = 0 for CA2 an input, = 1 for CA2 an output

Bits 4 to 7 act in a similar manner for CB1 and CB2. If CA2 is an output it can be programmed as either a level or a pulse. Bits 1 and 2 will then have different meanings:

Bit 1    If 0 when CA2 is a pulse, makes CA2 go to 0 when reading from or writing to Port A. It remains 0 until an active signal appears on CA1. If 1, makes CA2 go to 0 for one clock pulse when reading from or writing to Port A

Bit 2    If 0, CA2 is a pulse, if 1 CA2 is a level

As an example, we will assume that the following conditions are required for the four control lines:

CA1  input, active low to high transition

CA2  input, active low to high transition, normal mode (reset by reading or writing to Port A)

CB1  input, active high to low transition

CB2  output, pulse mode, giving pulse 1 clock period in duration

The bit pattern to be loaded into the peripheral control register will then be

| | |
|---|---|
| Bit 0 = 1 | CA1 active low to high |
| Bit 1 = 0 | CA2 in normal mode |
| Bit 2 = 1 | CA2 active low to high |
| Bit 3 = 0 | CA2 is input |
| Bit 4 = 0 | CB1 active high to low |
| Bit 5 = 1 | CB2 pulse is 1 clock period in duration |
| Bit 6 = 0 | CB2 is pulse |
| Bit 7 = 1 | CB2 is output |

The required pattern is 10100101 or A5 in hex.

The timers, the shift register, and the port input latches are controlled by the auxiliary control register (ACR). With a normal input transfer, the processor reads the data port and copies its contents into the accumulator. This requires the data to be available and unchanging when the read instruction is executed. When the input data is changing quickly, it will be necessary to take a sample of it when it is present and hold it until the read operation occurs. This can be done by using the latch input mode. A sample of input is taken when CA1 (for Port A) or CB1 (for Port B) is activated. The data is held ready for the processor until the next signal on the control line occurs. This latch mode is obtained by setting bit 0 (Port A) or bit 1 (Port B) of the ACR to 1. If they are cleared to 0 the normal input mode operates. Bits 2, 3 and 4 control the shift register, bit 5 controls timer 2, and bits 6 and 7 control timer 1.

Timer 2 can either count microprocessor clock pulses (bit 5 = 0) in the 'single shot' mode or count input pulses on bit 6 of Port B (bit 5 = 0). This action will override any other use of bit 6. The clock frequency is usually 1 MHz so that each cycle lasts 1 microsecond. The timer is a 16-bit register which is loaded with its low byte first. The high byte is loaded next and the register then begins to count down to zero, setting the timer 2 flag when this happens. The timer is frequently used to generate time delays and has the advantage that once the register has been loaded no further processor involvement is needed until the flag is set at the end of the delay period. An interrupt can then be created to initiate some action required after the delay.

To generate a time delay of 5 milliseconds with a clock frequency of 1 MHz, we need a count of 5000 or 1388 in hex. A suitable program would be:

| Instruction | Code | Comment |
|---|---|---|
| LDA #00 | A9 00 | Clear accumulator |
| STA E00C | 8D 0C E0 | Move to ACR to set single shot mode |
| LDA #88 | A9 88 | Load 88 into accumulator |
| STA E008 | 8D 08 E0 | Move to low byte of counter |
| LDA #13 | A9 13 | Load 13 into accumulator |
| STA E009 | 8D 08 E0 | Move to low byte of counter |

The timer starts counting down to zero after the last instruction is executed. The end of the delay can be detected either by a waiting loop which continually reads the timer flag and leaves the loop when it is set, or by arranging for the timer flag to create an interrupt.

By setting all ACR bits to zero we have assumed that the port input latches are not used, that the shift register is disabled, and that timer 1 is used to generate a single interrupt; for other conditions some bits of the ACR will be set, but bit 5 which controls timer 2 must be held at zero. The bits of the ACR control actions as follows:

| Bit | 7 | 6 | 5 | 4 | 3 | 2 | 1 | 0 |
|---|---|---|---|---|---|---|---|---|
| | T1 | T1 | T2 | SR | SR | SR | PB latch | PA latch |

Timer 1 can operate in four modes according to the settings of bits 6 and 7. These are

| ACR7 | ACR6 | |
|---|---|---|
| 0 | 0 | Generates a single interrupt each time T1 is loaded and counted down to zero |
| 0 | 1 | Generates continuous interrupts each time T1 is counted down to zero |

| 1 | 0 | Generates a single interrupt and a single pulse on PB7 each time T1 is loaded and counted down to zero |
| 1 | 1 | Generates continuous interrupts and a square-wave on PB7 |

The shift register uses CB1 for shift pulses and CB2 for data input and output, and has four input and four output modes. ACR4 is 0 for input and 1 for output. The modes are determined by ACR2 and ACR3 as follows:

| *ACR4* | *ACR3* | *ACR2* | |
|---|---|---|---|
| 0 | 0 | 0 | SR disabled, processor can read from or write to SR |
| 0 | 0 | 1 | Shift in under control of T2 low byte, clock pulses on CB1 |
| 0 | 1 | 0 | Shift in at system clock rate |
| 0 | 1 | 1 | Shift in under control of external pulses fed to CB1 |
| 1 | 0 | 0 | Free running shift out, rate controlled by T2 |
| 1 | 0 | 1 | Shift out controlled by T2, interrupt created after each 8 bits |
| 1 | 1 | 0 | Shift out at system clock rate |
| 1 | 1 | 1 | Shift out under control of external pulses fed to CB1 |

## 7.4   Z80 I/O Package

The parallel I/O package designed for the Z80 family, coded Z8420 or Z80 PIO, has two 8-bit data ports and two handshaking lines per port. It can be used in four different modes:

| | |
|---|---|
| Mode 0 | Byte Output |
| Mode 1 | Byte Input |
| Mode 2 | Bidirectional Byte |
| Mode 3 | Bit Input/Output |

Programming the PIO in the first three modes requires two words per port to be sent to the control register. The first of these is the mode control word and the second the interrupt vector for use in interrupt mode 2. The mode control word is identified by 1111 in the four LS bits. The two MS bits specify the mode and bits 4 and 5 are 'don't care' and may have any value. The byte thus has the following format:

| D7 | D6 | X | X | 1 | 1 | 1 | 1 |
|---|---|---|---|---|---|---|---|

D6 and D7 indicate the mode as in the table below:

| D7 | D6 | Mode | |
|----|----|------|---|
| 0 | 0 | 0 | Output |
| 0 | 1 | 1 | Input |
| 1 | 0 | 2 | Bidirectional |
| 1 | 1 | 3 | Bit |

The interrupt vector is identified by having a zero in the LS bit position. When an interrupt is granted it is assembled with the contents of the processor I register to give the address which holds the low byte of the address of the interrupt service routine. The next byte contains the high byte of the address of the routine.

Modes 0 and 1 have all bits of the port as output or inputs. Mode 2 allows Port A to have all bits acting either as inputs or outputs, but Port B cannot be used. One of the handshaking lines is an input (ASTB or BSTB) which is used to acknowledge the receipt of data or to strobe data into the port. The other line is an output (ARDY or BRDY) which indicates when output data is ready, or when the port can accept input from the peripheral device.

As an example, if Port A is required to accept a byte input (Mode 1), the Mode control Word is 01001111 (4F in hex) if 0 is written into the don't care bits D4 and D5. We assume that the four addresses which the PIO responds to are

| | |
|------|------|
| E000 | Data Port A |
| E001 | Data Port B |
| E002 | Control Input A |
| E003 | Control Input B |

The program needed to set up the PIO is then:

| Instruction | Code | Comment |
|-------------|------|---------|
| LD A, 4F | 3E 4F | Load Accumulator with 4F |
| LD (E002), A | 32 02 E0 | Transfer to Control A |
| LD A, XX | 3E XX | Load Accumulator with Int. Vector |
| LD (E002), A | 32 02 E0 | Transfer to Control A |

Here XX denotes the low byte of the interrupt vector which must be an even number.

If the PIO is used in Bit Mode, three control bytes are needed in addition to the mode control byte and the interrupt vector. These are

I/O Register Control Byte
Interrupt Control Byte
Mask Control Byte

The I/O register control byte acts like the data direction register of the 6821 package; each bit determines whether the corresponding port line is an input (bit = 1) or an output (bit = 0). The interrupt control byte has the format

| D7 | D6 | D5 | D4 | 0 | 1 | 1 | 1 |

If D4 = 0 no mask byte follows, if D4 = 1 mask byte follows
If D5 = 0 active level is low, if D5 = 1 active level is high
If D6 = 0 interrupt OR function, if D6 = 1 interrupt AND function
If D7 = 0 interrupt is disabled, if D7 = 1 interrupt is enabled

The byte is identified by the pattern 0111 in the four LS bits.

The way in which the bits are combined to generate an interrupt is determined by D6. If this is 0, a change to the active level in any monitored bit (the OR function) will create an interrupt; if it is 1, an interrupt occurs only if all monitored bits (the AND function) change to the active level.

The mask control byte determines which bits are monitored. They must have been programmed as inputs and also have a 0 in the corresponding position of the mask control byte.

Thus if the I/O register control byte is 11001100 and the mask control byte is 00111001, D2, D3, D6 and D7 are inputs. Of these only D2, D6 and D7 have a 0 in the mask control byte and so only these three will be monitored. If D5 of the interrupt control byte is 1 (active level high), D6 is 0 and D7 is 1, an interrupt will be created when any one of D2, D6 or D7 changes from 0 to 1. If D6 is 1 all three bits must change to 1 to create an interrupt. However, if D7 is 0 interrupts are disabled.

When reading from the PIO a complete byte is always input from the data port, although some of the bits may have been programmed for output. In this case the signal read from each output bit will be that which has just been written into it. The signal from each input will be that presented to the data port.

Finally, an interrupt disable byte can be sent at any time to control interrupts without affecting other registers. This byte has the format

| D7 | X | X | X | 0 | 0 | 1 | 1 |

If D7 = 0 interrupts are disabled, if D7 = 1 they are enabled.    X denotes a don't care bit.

## 7.5 Memory-Mapped Input/Output

Both the 6800 and the 6502 microprocessors are designed for 'memory-mapped' input/output addressing. This means that the registers in external packages or interfaces must share the total 64K address space with the program and data stores. Generally they do not use more than a few dozen locations and thus do not materially diminish the space available for storage. However, since there are 16 address lines some extra hardware may be needed for address decoding. The Z80 has an alternative provision for I/O addresses in which they do not share their address space with storage. A separate space of 256 addresses is available using the eight low-order address lines, by energising an IORQ (I/O request) line instead of the MEMRQ line which indicates a memory access.

Direct instructions for input and output are of the form

IN n     or     OUT n

Here n is the device address which is held in the second byte of the instruction. The only action possible is the transfer of data between the accumulator and the device. Register indirect addressing can also be used, with the device number held in register C. In this case data can be transferred to or from any of the processor 8-bit registers. The main advantage of memory-mapped I/O is that the full set of instructions is available to operate on the device registers, including increment, decrement, complement, logical, and arithmetic functions. This feature can reduce the length of some device service programs.

## 7.6    Examples of I/O Programming

The following example deals with a digital-to-analogue converter attached to a 6800 microprocessor via a PIA. The addresses for the PIA are

| | |
|---|---|
| PA,DDRA | 8004 |
| CRA | 8005 |
| PB, DDRB | 8006 |
| CRB | 8007 |

The DAC is connected to Port B and is required to generate a staircase waveform (as an approximation to a saw-tooth wave) whose period is controlled by a set of eight switches connected to Port A. The program reads the binary number set on the switches and counts this down to zero. It then increments Accumulator A, outputs its contents to the DAC, and returns to read the switches again. Accumulator A increments until it reaches 255 and the next increment brings it back to zero. The DAC output thus rises uniformly and then jumps back to zero, so generating a saw-tooth waveform.

| Instruction | Code | Comment |
|---|---|---|
| LDA A #04 | 86 04 | Load bit pattern for CRA |
| STA A 8005 | B7 80 05 | Transfer to CRA |
| COM 8006 | 73 80 06 | Set DDRB for output (all bits 1) |
| LDA A #24 | 86 24 | Load bit pattern for CRB |
| STA A 8007 | B7 80 07 | Transfer to CRB |
| STEP: INC A | 4C | Increment Accumulator A |
| STA A 8006 | B7 80 06 | Set new value into DAC |
| LDA B 8004 | F6 80 04 | Read switch setting into Acc. B |
| LOOP: DEC B | 5A | Decrement Accumulator B |
| NOP | 01 | No operation (delay of 2 clock cycles) |
| NOP | 01 | No operation |
| BNE LOOP | 26 FB | Return to LOOP if not zero |
| BRA STEP | 20 F2 | Branch back to STEP |

The first five instructions set up the PIA; the remainder form a loop which runs indefinitely.

A program performing the same action with a Z80 is given below.

| Instruction | Code | Comment |
|---|---|---|
| LD A, #0F | 3E 0F | Fetch bit pattern for Port output |
| OUT 7 | D3 07 | Transfer to Mode Control Reg. A |
| LD A, #4F | 3E 4F | Fetch bit pattern for Port input |
| OUT 6 | D3 06 | Transfer to Mode Control Reg. B |
| START: IN 4 | DB 04 | Read number from switches into Acc. |
| DEC: DEC A | 3D | Decrement Accumulator |
| JRNZ DEC | 20 FD | Repeat till zero |
| INC B | 04 | Then increment Register B |
| LD A, B | 78 | Transfer B to Accumulator |
| OUT 5 | D3 05 | Output to DAC |
| JR START | 18 F5 | Return to START |

Here the Port addresses are

| Port A | Control | 07 | Port B | Control | 06 |
|---|---|---|---|---|---|
|  | Data (DAC) | 05 |  | Data (switches) | 04 |

The Accumulator reads the switch number and is decremented to zero to generate a delay and Register B holds the number fed to the DAC.

# 8 Aids to Program Writing and Testing

## 8.1 The Use of Assemblers

In the programs listed in previous sections of this book we have shown both the instructions in mnemonic form and the corresponding machine code in hex notation. It is convenient to begin with the program in mnemonic form as this makes it much easier to read and to amend later on. It is, however, necessary to convert it to machine code before it can be run. When writing small programs the conversion can be performed manually, but it becomes a much more tedious process for longer programs. The tedium is much reduced, as is the chance of making mistakes, if the conversion is done by a computer program. Such a program is called an *Assembler*. Although each instruction in mnemonic form generates a corresponding instruction in machine code, the assembler needs to recognise other commands which inform it of the location into which the first instruction is to be loaded, where to reserve storage for variables, etc. These extra commands are called assembler directives or pseudo-operation statements where they affect the operation of the assembler, and assignment statements where they identify a name with a value or an address. Thus the command which tells the assembler where to load the first instruction in the machine code program (the program origin) is

ORG 1000

This would start the program in location 1000. To allow for additions and alterations, subroutines may be spaced, say, 100 bytes from the preceding program. If this ends at location 1590, we can provide the gap by writing ORG 1700 at the top of the subroutine. Variables can have initial values assigned to them by assignment statements such as

COUNT    EQU    10

Where programs start with such statements the first executable instruction may be some way down the program. When we run the program we must specify where to start execution, usually by including the command

ENT $

86

The symbol $ is often used to denote the address of the current instruction, so we can use it in an instruction such as

JR   $+6

This will cause the program to branch to a location 6 bytes beyond the current instruction.

Some assemblers which operate with a file store facility need a title to be specified in the first line so that the source program can be identified on the backing store and recalled when needed.

A typical assembler will have provision for four separate items or fields on each line, namely

Label      Operation      Address      Comment

Usually a separator symbol, such as a colon, is required after the label, and another one before the comment (usually a semi-colon). The comment is printed in full in a listing of the source program, but otherwise ignored. One of the main advantages of assemblers, as with high level languages like BASIC, is that addresses and variables can be given names and these can be used in the program. Also constants can be specified in binary, decimal, or hexadecimal with suitable symbols. Names used for variables must have their addresses specified, but this is not necessary for labels which identify instruction addresses.

## 8.2   Example of Assembly

The following small program illustrates some of the features of an assembler. It subtracts in decimal notation two numbers which have been entered in BCD form, using immediate addressing. The result is loaded into location 1000 which can be examined after running the program, and will contain the number 18.

Pass 1      errors: 00

| Loc. | Code | No. | | Instruction | | Comment |
|------|------|-----|--------|-------|---------|---------|
| 3000 | | 10 | | ORG | #3000 | |
| 3000 | | 20 | START: | ENT | $ | ; program start |
| 3000 | 3E46 | 30 | | LD | A,#46 | ; first no. |
| 3002 | 0628 | 40 | | LD | B,#28 | ; second no. |
| 3004 | 90 | 50 | | SUB | B | ; subtract nos |
| 3005 | 27 | 60 | | DAA | | ; decimal adjust |
| 3006 | 320010 | 70 | | LD | (1000),A | ; store result |
| 3009 | C9 | 80 | | RET | | ; return to minitor |

Pass 2      errors: 00
START      3000

The first three columns are entered by the computer; the remainder is typed in by the programmer. The use of the # symbol in the ORG instruction denotes hexadecimal notation, omitting it causes the assembler to treat is as a decimal number. The first column shows the location (in hex) of the first byte of the instruction, the second column contains the machine code, and the third column is a serial number to allow each line to be identified for alteration if needed. Extra lines can be added later and they will automatically be displayed in numerical order when a listing is requested. The built-in option for line numbers is to start at 10 and increment each time by 10. These numbers can be changed if needed. Another instruction can be entered between, say, Nos 30 and 40 by giving it any serial number between 30 and 40.

Most assemblers provide a variety of options; when the program is first written it is likely to contain some errors and before we can obtain an output from the assembler we must remove these. So, initially, we do not need a program listing or the generation of hexadecimal code; by omitting these the assembler will run much faster. The assembler will, however, always report the number of errors. When the number of errors has been reduced to zero we can call for another assembler run which can print out the program in source and object form and provide a symbol table. This is a list of all of the names used for variables and labels, together with the locations in which they are stored. In the above example we have only one entry, the label START which corresponds to location 3000. This example was produced on a Z80 system, but there is an advantage in using a larger computer with more internal and backing store.

## 8.3   Cross-assemblers and Editors

The assembly process can be speeded up and more facilities provided by running the assembler on a minicomputer or mainframe machine. In such a case it is called a 'cross-assembler' since the machine code output runs on the target microprocessor, not on the machine which executes the assembler program. This procedure involves the operating system of the minicomputer and the various utility programs which it includes. The process starts with the generation of a file which holds the source program in assembly language, using a text editor which usually numbers the lines and at the end of the session saves the program on the backing store. This program is then submitted to the cross-assembler and any errors noted. An advantage of using a larger machine is that the error messages can be more detailed, making it easier to find the errors. By contrast the limited storage available in a microprocessor system usually means that the only information given is an error number, and a list must be consulted to find the nature of the fault. Since it is unlikely that the first attempt at assembly will give no errors, it is necessary to revert to the editor to amend the program and remove the errors. This process may have to be repeated several times before all errors have been eliminated. When an error-free assembly has been obtained, the source program can be stored for future reference, together with the machine code version. In some systems the machine code program may also be loaded into a ROM which will form part of a prototype microprocessor system, or punched onto paper tape for a semiconductor manufacturer to build into a masked ROM.

The following session produces a program for double-length multiplication on a 6800 microprocessor. The format of the instructions is similar to that of the Z80, but a space is the only separator needed between fields. Also, if an asterisk is typed into column 1 the rest of the line is available for comment. Hex values are indicated by the symbols x'. The prompt from the operating system is % and from the editor >. The editor is called by the command em, and the cross-assembler by the command mas followed by the name of the source file (dlmult). The user must initially log on to the system and then the operating system gives the prompt % to indicate that it expects a command. The first call is to the editor to add the text to a blank file created by the command f dimult which also names the file. In the following listing the computer-generated text is under-lined, the rest of the text has been typed in by the programmer.

| | | |
|---|---|---|
| % em | (calls editor program) | |
| Editor | | |
| > f dlmult | (creates and names file) | |
| dlmult | | |
| > a | (command to append text) | |

```
***   PROGRAM TITLE DLMULT   ***
**    This program multiplies x by y and gives          **
**    a double-length product. Acc. A holds             **
**    product high byte and Acc. B product low byte     **
*
x        EQU    x'10
y        EQU    x'11
prodh    EQU    x'12
prodl    EQU    x'13
*
         org    x'20
*
clr      a                    clear for prodh
         clr    b             clear for prodl
loop     add    b     x       add x to running total
         adc    a     %x'00   add carry to Acc. A
         dec    y             decrement y
         bne    loop          repeat if y not zero
         sta    a     prodh   store high byte of product
         sta    b     prodl   store low byte of product
         swi                  halt
```

| | |
|---|---|
| . | (return to editor) |
| >w | (write file to disc) |
| 498 | (no. of bytes in file) |
| >q | (quit editor, return to operating system) |
| % mas dlmult | (call cross-assembler) |
| Pass 1 dlmult | |
| dlmult: | |
|    13 syntax | (error message, line 13) |
| % em dlmult | (return to editor to correct error) |
| Editor | |
| 498 | |
| >13p | (print line containing error) |
| clr    a | |
| >13 d | (delete line 13) |
| >12 a | (insert correct line) |
|         clr    a        clear for prodh | |
| . | (end correction) |
| >w | (write corrected version back to disc) |
| 516 | |
| >q | (quit editor, return to operating system) |
| % mas dlmult | (call cross-assembler again) |
| Pass 1 | |
| dlmult | |
| Pass 2 | |
| dlmult | (no errors signalled) |
| % | (cross-assembler returns to operating system) |

In this example the 13th line was typed in wrongly as the op. code was entered into the field reserved for the label. The simplest way to correct this is to delete the faulty line and add the correct version after line 12. The dot symbol is used to terminate the insertion of new text and return to the editor. The amended program then assembles without error. The output is put into a file which can be printed out as a record, or the hexadecimal program can be sent to a PROM programmer to load it into a user-programmable store. The printed listing adds the location and the hex code for each instruction and a symbol table, as shown below.

*** PROGRAM TITLE DLMULT ***

**   This program multiplies x by y and gives     **

**   a double-length product. Acc. A holds      **

**   product high byte and Acc. B product low byte  **

*

| | | | |
|---|---|---|---|
| 0010 | x | EQU | x'10 |
| 0011 | y | EQU | x'11 |

|      | 0012 | prodh | EQU | x'12 |        |                           |
|------|------|-------|-----|------|--------|---------------------------|
|      | 0013 | prodl | EQU | x'13 |        |                           |
|      |      | *     |     |      |        |                           |
| 0020 |      |       | org | x'20 |        |                           |
|      |      | *     |     |      |        |                           |
| 0020 | 4F   |       | clr | a    |        | clear for prodh           |
| 0021 | 5F   |       | clr | b    |        | clear for prodl           |
| 0022 | DB 10 | loop | add | b    | x      | add x to running total    |
| 0024 | 89 00 |      | adc | a    | %x'00  | add carry to Acc. A       |
| 0026 | 7A 0011 |    | dec | y    |        | decrement y               |
| 0029 | 26 F7 |      | bne | loop |        | repeat if y not zero      |
| 002B | 97 12 |      | sta | a    | prodh  | store high byte of product |
| 002D | D7 13 |      | sta | b    | prodl  | store low byte of product  |
| 002F | 3F    |      | swi |      |        | halt                      |
|      |      | *     |     |      |        |                           |
| loop | 0020 |       | prodh | 0012 |      | prodl    0013             |
| x    | 0010 |       | y   | 0011 |        |                           |

This program has a loop and by using the label 'loop' we can avoid calculating the offset needed in the branch instruction, leaving the assembler to supply it. This saves a good deal of effort if we need to insert or delete an instruction in the loop, particularly if the loop is nested. We must only remember to re-assemble after each alteration. This particular assembler has a helpful feature in that when jumping to a subroutine it can use a branch instruction if the move is less than 128 bytes from the current location, and a jump instruction with extended addressing if the move is longer.

The operating system used in the above example is UNIX, originally developed by two research workers at the Murray Hill Computer Center of Bell Laboratories in the USA. It was originally written in assembly language, but in order to simplify maintenance and extension a high level language called 'C' was subsequently produced. This language is now available on many microprocessors and is used for system programming quite apart from its use with UNIX.

UNIX was designed by users and consequently it presents a much simpler interface to the user than do many other operating systems. For example, most of the programs available in the library can be called up by typing only two letters. Where these are required to operate on users' programs, they must of course be followed by the name of the file containing the program. For example, to call up the editor initially, before we have generated a file we need only type

em

but to edit the file dlmult subsequently we type

em dlmult

In addition to the two commands em and mas used in the example, the following list includes others that are frequently needed:

| | |
|---|---|
| dir | obtain directory |
| fc | call Fortran compiler |
| fi | list file names in the directory |
| ls | list contents of directory |
| ss | get system state |
| rm name | remove file called name |
| lf name | print file called name |
| basic | call up Basic interpreter |
| date | displays data and time |

UNIX also provides for mailbox facilities, enabling any user to send a message to any other user, using his login password as the address. To read one's own mail needs the command mail.

The more frequently used commands in the editor program are found in the example; a 'help' feature is also provided which displays a list of all commands available by typing h.

## 8.4    The Use of Macros

One advantage of some assemblers, particularly the larger ones which run on minicomputers, is that they support what are called 'macro-instructions' or macros. These are groups of instructions that can be incorporated into a program by a single statement. They resemble subroutines, but instead of including one copy in the program which can be called a number of times, the instructions contained in the macro are copied into the program each time the macro is called. They are used for a small group of instructions where the extra time involved in jumping to a subroutine and returning from it would be worth saving.

The macro is defined by a statement such as

DEFM   DLADD

This is followed by the instructions which comprise the macro, and ends with a statement such as

ENDM

The macro would be invoked by the word DLADD.

## 8.5   Disassemblers

We are sometimes faced with programs in machine code which we need to analyse or amend. This would be much easier if the program were written in assembly language. Programs are available to perform the conversion from machine code to assembly language, called *disassemblers*. Although they recognise all of the mnemonics for the op. codes, they cannot have any knowledge of the program application and so cannot devise variable names which indicate the quantity they represent. Typically no names will be allocated to variables, which are identified by their addresses, but where labels are needed, for example to identify the destination of a jump, they may be coded with the label address. Thus when writing a loop we may label the first instruction START, and the branch instruction at the end of the loop may be BNE START. If the address of the label START is 500 it would be disassembled as L500 and the end of the loop would be disassembled to BNE L500.

A major problem in disassembly arises if there are text messages embedded in the program. The disassembler will try to convert these back into instructions and so may generate nonsense. Most disassemblers have facilities for the user to specify which parts of the program are text; these are then copied into the output without alteration.

## 8.6   Linker Program

When programs are prepared on larger machines with plenty of backing store it is convenient to store a library of subroutines and program segments on disc which can be incorporated into new programs and thus reduce the effort required to write them. To do this the output of the assembler must be in a 'relocatable' form, that is it must be possible to load it at any convenient part of the store. In order to add the modules from the library another program called a 'linker' is used. This adjusts the addresses so that the assembly output and the library modules form one continuous program with the correct links between the various segments.

## 8.7   Using Single Shot and Breakpoint Facilities

One of the features which distinguishes a microprocessor system from a larger computer is the complete absence of any monitoring facilities which could, for instance, display the contents of registers and locations in the store. Thus if we wish to test a program before committing it to a read only store, we must use a special development system which has facilities for loading the program into a writable store and running it under the control of the operator. This system will have a monitor program which allows the operator to load and inspect any location in the store, and control execution of the program. One of the major provisions allows the program to be executed an instruction at a time, usually called 'single shot' operation.

Most monitor programs allow all internal registers to be examined after each instruction, and also a section of the main store. Since many errors arise from incorrect destinations for branch or jump instructions, the ability to track the contents of the program counter and so discover the order in which instructions are obeyed will allow most errors to be located. However, the single shot feature becomes of limited value when we encounter a loop, perhaps to produce a time delay, which is executed a thousand or more times. If we can easily modify the program we can change the loop counter to, say, three. This will not cause us to waste much time traversing the loop. If the program cannot easily be changed we can first check for errors until we reach the loop. We can put a 'breakpoint' at the instruction following the loop. If we now run the program at normal speed it will execute the loop and then stop at the breakpoint. We can then continue single shot operation as before. Some monitor programs allow many breakpoints, others only one which must be moved as program testing continues.

# 9 Single Chip Microprocessors

## 9.1 The Single Chip Market

A few years after the first 8-bit microprocessor were put onto the market, manufacturers realised that there was a considerable demand for small systems for building into domestic products, test gear, and simple control systems. Since price was a major factor in deciding whether an application was feasible, the fewer chips needed for the system the better. A major reduction in the chip count can be obtained by putting all the components needed for a microcomputer on a single chip, and this policy was adopted by several manufacturers. Early single chip microprocessors had typically 1K bytes of program store and 64 bytes of RAM, but later versions have more storage and some can address a total of 64K bytes.

Typical of the early devices is the 8000 series, comprising the 8020, 8021, and 8022. The 8020 has 1K bytes of ROM, 64 bytes of RAM, 13 I/O lines, and a counter/timer. The 8021 has 8 more I/O lines and a zero crossing detector. The 8022 has 2K bytes of ROM, 28 I/O lines, an 8-bit A/D converter, a zero crossing detector, and provision for interrupts. None of the three can have additional ROM or RAM attached. Somewhat later the 48 series followed, and was widely used and available from several manufacturers.

## 9.2 The 48 Series of Microprocessors

Initially there were three models: the 8048 which has 1K of mask ROM, 64 bytes of RAM and 27 I/O lines; the 8035 which has no ROM and is intended for use with external ROM; and the 8748 which has 1K of user-programmable (EPROM) storage. All three models appear identical to the programmer. Subsequent versions provided up to 4K bytes of ROM and 256 bytes of RAM. The architecture of these microprocessors is somewhat different from that of the Z80. There are eight 8-bit registers which are directly addressable, but no register pair operations. The first two of these, R0 and R1, can be used as pointers to the rest of the RAM. Thus in an instruction we can address the first eight bytes of RAM directly, and the rest of the RAM indirectly. To copy the accumulator contents to R3 the instruction is

MOV R3, A

However, to move the accumulator contents to RAM location 20 we must first load the address 20 into a pointer register, say R0. The instructions needed are then

MOV R0, #20
MOV @R0, A

The first of these is a 'Load Immediate' instruction to put the constant 20 into R0. In addition to a full set of instructions for moving data, there are two unusual data exchange instructions:

XCH A, Rn
and        XCH A, @R

Here n can have any value from 0 to 7, and R denotes R0 to R1. The first instruction exchanges the contents of the accumulator and Rn, and the second exchanges the contents of the accumulator and a RAM location pointed to by R.

The arithmetic and logical instructions are fewer than those provided for the other microprocessors we have examined, and comprise

Add
Add with carry
AND
OR
XOR
Increment
Decrement
Clear
Complement
Decimal adjust
Rotate left
Rotate left through carry
Rotate right
Rotate right through carry
Swap nibbles

In all of these operations the accumulator is the source of one operand and the result is left in the accumulator. The 'swap nibbles' instruction exchanges bits 0 to 3 and 4 to 7 of the accumulator, and acts as a 'swap digits' instruction for BCD data. Note that there is no subtract instruction; to subtract X from Y we must

Move X to accumulator
Complement the accumulator    (1's complement)

Increment accumulator   (gives 2's complement of X)
Add Y   (gives Y − X)

The add, add with carry and the logical operations have three address modes: register, register indirect, and immediate.

Transfers to and from external devices can occur via two data ports or the data bus, all 8 bits wide. In addition to transferring data, logical AND and OR operations can be programmed between either ports or the bus and an immediate operand. These enable specific port lines to be set and cleared without disturbing the other lines. For example, if we are concerned with bit 2 of Port 1, we can set it by using the OR instruction on Port 1 with the immediate operand 00000100 (04 in hex) which has 1 in the bit 2 position and zeros elsewhere. The instruc-- tion is

ORL P1 #04

To clear the same bit we use the logical AND instruction, but with the operand 11111011 (FB in hex) which has a zero in bit 2 position and 1 else- where. The instruction for this is

ANL P1 #FB

### 9.3   Branch and Control Instructions

The 48 series has a variety of jump instructions, all but one of which specify an absolute address. The exception is the Jump Indirect in which the address is held in the accumulator. Conditional jumps which test flag states are

Jump if Carry = 1
Jump if Carry = 0
Jump if Accumulator = 0
Jump if Accumulator not 0
Jump if T0 = 1
Jump if T0 = 0
Jump if T1 = 1
Jump if T1 = 0
Jump if F0 = 1
Jump if F1 = 1
Jump if Timer Flag = 1

T0 and T1 are two input lines which allow the state of external devices to be tested, F0 and F1 are flags which can be set or cleared by program.

Any register can be used as a loop counter and a single instruction provides loop control. Its action is to decrement the selected register and if the result is non-zero to jump to a prescribed address (normally the start of the loop). A bit-testing instruction allows the programmer to test the state of any specified bit of the accumulator. The three MS bits of the instruction specify a bit of the accumulator and the microprocessor jumps to the address in the second byte of the instruction if this bit is set. This feature allows the state of external sensors and switches to be determined without having to rotate or shift an input byte so that a particular bit moves into the carry position.

The counter/timer can either generate a time interval by counting clock pulses, or count external events via the T1 input.

## 9.4    Single Chip Versions of the 6800

The 8048 series of single chip microprocessors was given quite different architecture from its predecessors, the 8085 and 8080. In contrast the basic 6800 processor was used as the central element in the 6801, 6803, and 6805. These all have internal RAM and ROM and parallel ports to connect to external devices, and use the same basic instruction set as the original 6800. Their particular features are

6801 2K bytes ROM, 128 bytes RAM, serial and parallel interfaces, timer, 8 bit X 8 bit multiplier

6803 A sub-set of the 6801

6805 P2  1100 bytes of ROM, 64 bytes of RAM, 20 I/O lines, zero crossing detector, counter/timer

Other versions of the 6805 have more ROM and an 8-bit ADC

The 6801 has a few extra instructions to control the multiplier and the timer

## 9.5    The Z8 Family of Microprocessors

The Z8 family of single chip microprocessors was introduced some years after the Z80 and has an architecture designed to simplify control applications. The first three members are

Z8601 2K bytes ROM, 128 bytes RAM, 32 I/O lines, two 8-bit counter/timers, UART (Universal Asynchronous Receiver/Transmitter for serial data transfers to and from data terminals, VDUs, teleprinters, etc.)

Z8602 Similar to Z8601 but without ROM. This is intended for building prototypes using external ROM

Z8603 This is similar to the Z8602 but has a socket for plugging in a 2K byte PROM for development work

There are three more members, the Z8611, Z8612, and Z8613, which are identical to the Z8601/2/3 but have 4K bytes of ROM

In addition to the 128 bytes of RAM, all of these microprocessors have a 144-byte register file. 124 bytes of this are general-purpose registers and the remainder are 4 port registers and 16 status and control registers. One of these is the register pointer which allows any one of the registers to be addressed indirectly.

The instruction set is comprehensive, including Add, Add with Carry, Subtract, Subtract with Carry, Decimal Adjust, Increment, and Decrement. The latter two operations can be performed on 16-bit as well as 8-bit operands. There is a Stack Pointer for stack operations. The stack can be in RAM, in the register file, or in external RAM. The state of any bit can be tested by using the mask operation TM #nn. This generates the local AND operation between the contents of a register and the immediate operand #nn, and sets or clears the zero and sign flags accordingly. The contents of the register are not affected.

Thus if we are concerned with bit 3 of a register, we use the operand 00001000 or 08 in hex in place of nn. If the Z flag is subsequently set, bit 3 is 1; if not, bit 3 is 0. 15 conditional jump instructions are provided and one unconditional jump. These can have absolute or relative addresses.

# 10  16-bit Microprocessors

## 10.1  The Limitations of 8-bit Microprocessors

Current 8-bit microprocessors have been developed steadily for over a decade and now provide a rich instruction set and a high rate of computation. Despite this the 8-bit data bus and the 16-bit address bus impose a limitation to the volume of program and data that can be handled conveniently. The 8-bit data limitation means that single-byte arithmetic is not sufficiently accurate for many purposes, since each item can be specified with a resolution no better than 1 part in 256, and rounding-off errors steadily worsen this resolution as more arithmetic is performed. Thus many operations must be carried out with double-length numbers. This more than doubles the execution time of the program and increases the program storage space. Floating point numbers may consist of 24 or 32 bits for the significant digits and 8 bits to position the binary point; handling these will be much slower than 8-bit arithmetic.

The 16-bit address bus means that only 64K bytes of program space can be addressed directly; if more program space is needed, extra hardware must be used to allow the microprocessor to switch between 64K banks of storage, so slowing down access to instructions.

For these reasons it became clear that where both fast calculation and accuracy were needed a larger word size was essential. The most convenient step was to double the width of the data bus, the internal buses and the arithmetic unit, so producing a 16-bit microprocessor.

## 10.2  The Intel 8086 and 8088

The first of these to gain wide acceptance was the Intel 8086. This had some resemblance to the 8080 in having a single accumulator and other general-purpose registers, but had a much greater range of instructions and addressing modes. It was also given a 20-bit address bus, so that it could directly address 1 megabyte of storage. The combination of a larger instruction set and a larger word size gives the 8086 about 10 times the computing power of the 8080. The 8088 is a simplified 8086 which has exactly the same instruction set and internal 16-bit bus, but only an 8-bit data bus to external devices. This allows it to use all the interface packages designed for the 8080 and 8085 but slows down access to data and program. The computing power of the 8088 is consequently about 70 per cent of that of the 8086.

The register complement of the 8086 is shown in figure 10.1. The four data registers are AX the accumulator, BX the base register, CX the count register, and DX the data register. All of these can be split into two 8-bit registers; for example, AX can be split into AH the high-order byte and AL the low-order byte. The ALU can handle either 8-bit or 16-bit operands. BX is often used to access tables when it contains the address of the first item. Other items are accessed by using an offset in each instruction. CX can be used as a counter in loop operations and DX is used in multiplication and division operations and to hold the port address in I/O operations.

The pointer and index registers are used for addressing indirectly. SP is the stack pointer which acts conventionally and points to the top of the stack, and is used by the POP and PUSH instructions. BP is a base pointer used to address other areas of the stack. SI and DI are index registers used for indirect addressing and in string operations.

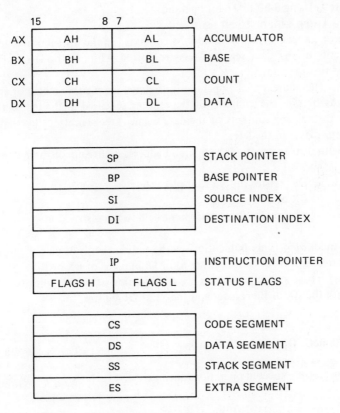

Figure 10.1  Register set of 8086 microprocessor.

At any time when a program is running there are four sections of storage accessible, identified by the segment registers CS, DS, SS, and ES. These each contain the addresses of the first item in the segment which may contain up to 65K bytes. CS, the code segment register, addresses the program. Its 16-bit contents are loaded into the top 16 bits of the 20-bit program counter and the value of the instruction pointer (IP) is added to it to determine the effective address of the next instruction. DS points to the data segment where variables are stored, SS points to the stack area, and ES to an extra area generally used for data.

## 10.3  Addressing Modes

In view of the variety of pointer, index and segment registers available in the 8086 there is scope for a greater range of address modes than are found in most 8-bit microprocessors. The modes are

Immediate — Using 8-bit or 16-bit operand.

Register — Using 8-bit or 16-bit register.

Absolute or direct — The 16-bit address contained in the instruction is added to the contents of the data segment register shifted 4 bits to the left to find the address of the operand.

Indirect — The address of the operand is obtained from either a base or an index register. As before, the contents of the register specified in the instruction are added to the current contents of the data segment register after these have been shifted four places to the left.

Indirect with displacement — The operand address is the sum of three items:

> DS register shifted four places left
> BX or BP register
> 8-bit or 16-bit displacement held in the instruction

Indirect, indexed — This is identical to the indirect with displacement, except that the internal register used is either SI or DI in place of BX or BP.

Indirect with base and index — This is a combination of the two previous modes. It uses both the BX or BP register and the SI or DI register.

## 10.4  Arithmetic Operations

In addition to the expected operations such as

> Add
> Add with Carry

Increment
Subtract
Subtract with Borrow
Decrement
Negate

there are others for adjusting the results of these when the operands are in BCD form. The speed of complex calculations is much increased by a built-in multiplier/divider which provides for integer and unsigned multiplication, and division and adjustment to the results when the numbers are encoded in BCD format.

The success of the 8086 encouraged the manufacturers to produce more powerful versions. Among these are the 80186 and 80188 which have a higher clock frequency and other improvements which give them about twice the power of the 8086 and 8088. Later came the 80286 which has a yet higher clock frequency and can address 16 megabytes of storage; it is estimated to have a power up to 6 times greater than the 8086.

## 10.5 The Z8000 Family of Microprocessors

The Zilog Z8000 family has two CPUs, the Z8001 and Z8002, which use the same instruction set and differ only in the storage space they can directly address. This is 8 megabytes for the Z8001 and 64 kilobytes for the Z8002. They have sixteen general-purpose 16-bit registers, any one of which can be used as an accumulator, and all but one can be used as index registers or address pointers. They can be used with a variety of formats; for example, the first eight 16-bit registers (R0 to R7) can be used for byte operations as each can be treated as two 8-bit registers. Thus R0 is divided into RL0, the low byte, and RH0, the high byte. Also, each pair of 16-bit registers can be used together as a 32-bit register, so that R0 and R1 are combined as RR0, R2 and R3 as RR2, etc. Finally, registers can be grouped in fours to handle 64 bits, so that R0, R1, R2 and R3 give RQ0, R4, R5, R6 and R7 give RQ4 etc. The various options are shown in figure 10.2 for the Z8002. The last register, R15, is duplicated; R15 is the Normal Stack Pointer and R15' the System Stack Pointer. The Z8002 also has 16-bit registers for the program counter, a flag and control word, and a program area status pointer (used in handling interrupts).

Z8000 instructions can handle bits, BCD digits (4 bits), bytes (8 bits), words (2 bytes), and long words (4 bytes) which can be held in processor registers or the main store. They can also operate on strings of words or bytes up to 64K bytes long, but these can only be held in the main store.

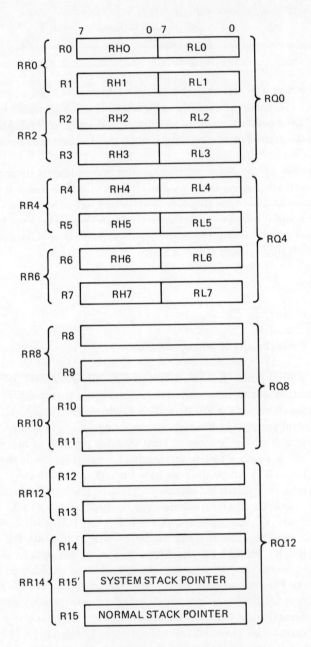

Figure 10.2  Z8002 general-purpose registers.

The addressing modes are broadly similar to those of the 8086 but involve adding only two items together. The modes permitted are:

> Immediate
> Register
> Register Indirect
> Direct

Index — The instruction specifies a register which contains the displacement; this is added to the base address also in the instruction to give the effective address of the operand.

Relative — The instruction contains a displacement which is added to the program counter to give the effective address.

Base — The instruction contains a displacement which is added to the contents of the base address. This is held in a register specified in the instruction.

Base Index — The instruction specifies two registers; one contains the displacement, the other the address which holds the base address. The base address is added to the displacement to find the address of the operand.

## 10.6 Z8000 Arithmetic Instructions

The range of arithmetic and local operations which the Z8000 processors can perform is broadly similar to that of the 8086, but as it can handle 8-bit and 16-bit operands nearly all instructions have two versions to cope with both lengths. Moreover, some can also handle 32-bit long words, so needing a third version of the instruction. These operations include:

> Load Memory
> Load Register
> Pop
> Push
> Add
> Compare
> Divide
> Multiply
> Subtract

There are in all 28 rotate and shift instructions, since nearly all of the rotate instructions can have 8-bit or 16-bit operands, and the shifts can have 8-bit or 32-bit operands.

Input/output operations can handle either 8-bit or 16-bit operands. This allows cheaper 8-bit peripheral packages designed for the 8080 and 8085 to be used for simpler transfers where 8-bit operands suffice. The I/O instructions provide for both data transfer and some arithmetic operations. Thus for input transfers the address into which the data is loaded can be incremented or decremented ready for the next transfer. For block transfers the contents of a register used for counting can also be decremented and the transfer will continue until the count has reached zero.

The Z8000 family is designed to allow multiple microprocessor systems and there are four instructions to control inter processor transfers.

### 10.7  The Motorola 68000 Microprocessor

The 68000 was originally developed as a 16-bit microprocessor, but subsequently a version (68008) with an 8-bit data bus was produced, followed by the 68010 with a 32-bit bus. The 68000 has sixteen 32-bit registers, eight (D0 to D7) for data or indexing and a second eight (A0 to A7) for addresses. The last of the address registers, A7, is duplicated and provides two stack pointers, one for the user mode and the other for use in supervisor mode. There is also a 16-bit status (flag) register and a 24-bit program counter, which permits direct addressing of 16 megabytes of storage space. The register complement is shown in figure 10.3. This is considerably more than most other 16-bit processors can address directly, and gives the 68000 an advantage in applications where a large volume of program or data must be accessed rapidly. The following address modes are provided:

Immediate — Operand is the next 8, 16 or 32 bits of the instruction.
Register Direct — Operand is the contents of a data or address register.
Absolute — Operand address is in next 1 or 2 words of instruction.
Relative — To PC with offset (16 bit) or with index and 8-bit offset.
Register Indirect — Operand address is in an address register, with optional post-increment or pre-decrement.
Register Indirect with offset — Operand address is the sum of an address register contents and a 16-bit offset.
Indexed Register Indirect with offset — Operand address is the sum of the contents of an address register and an index register and an 8-bit offset.

The immediate mode allows for either a byte, a word, or a long word to be loaded into a register. The relative address mode allows for indexing as well as the usual offset which is part of the instruction. In this case, as in all other modes which use a register, part of the instruction is used to specify which register is used. The register indirect mode can be used for accessing tables as well as blocks of data. In the latter case it is convenient to use the post-incrementing feature which automatically increments the register contents after each access, ready for the next item. This assumes that the data is accessed from the lowest address upwards. If the highest address is accessed first, the pre-decrement option must be used.

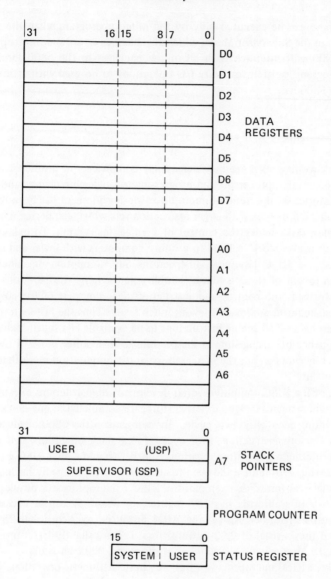

Figure 10.3 M68000 registers.

The 68000 is designed to allow several programs to be held in the microprocessor at the same time, each having the use of the system for a short period in
turn. Thus, users at several terminals can access the system simultaneously. In
order to prevent one user program from interfering with another, the system
normally operates in the User Mode in which Stop and Reset instructions are not

allowed. These can be executed only by the monitor program when the microprocessor is in the Supervisor Mode, which also handles errors and interrupts.

The 68000 will interface with all of the packages in the 6800 family, so allowing programs written for 6800 I/O operations to be used with little alteration on the 68000.


## 10.8  RISC systems

In this book we have examined an increasingly complex set of products, starting with three basic microprocessors and progressing to single chip devices and 16-bit systems. Historically, the trend of microprocessor development has been towards more complicated devices with larger instruction sets which can perform increasingly complex tasks under the control of a single instruction. To balance this picture there is also work in hand to produce computers with fewer and simpler instructions: the RISC (Reduced Instructions Set Computer) machines. The argument in favour of these is that by simplifying the range of operations which can be performed, the control and instruction decoding part of the computer can be much reduced and made to work much faster. Thus the faster stores now available can be used to enable instructions to be available at a much higher rate. The consequence of having simpler instructions is that rather more of them are needed for a given task, but the increased speed of computation more than compensates for this.

In most of the RISC computers so far developed, all instructions except Load and Store, which need access to external store, are completed in one clock cycle; Load and Store need only two cycles. By comparison the 6800 needs at least two cycles for any instruction, four cycles for a stack operation, and six for shifting or rotating a given store location. Another way in which RISC machines speed processing is to reduce the need to access external storage by having many more internal registers. For example, the RISC I microprocessor developed by the University of California has 137 registers of which 32 can be accessed by each subroutine. Another device, the ARM produced by Acorn, has 25 32-bit registers and uses a total of 25 000 transistors. It has a slightly faster processing speed than the Motorola 68020 which uses about 192 000 transistors.

Typically, a RISC microprocessor has only basic arithmetic operations such as addition and subtraction with and without carry, AND, OR, and XOR logical operations and shifts. Negate, complement, increment, and decrement must be programmed, as must multiply and divide. Only two address modes are provided, relative to the PC and relative to a base register. All instructions are conditional, four bits being allocated in each instruction to specify the test.

Generally, RISC devices simplify the programmer's task as he has fewer instructions and fewer address modes to remember. Some devices are designed for use with high level languages such as Pascal or C. These will help program writing, but fault finding will still need a knowledge of assembly language or machine code.

# 11   The 68000 Instruction Set

## 11.1   Introduction

Although the 68000 bears some family resemblance to the 6800, its designers took full advantage of the benefits of large-scale integration and 16-bit architecture to provide many more internal registers. This allows many variables to be held in the processor itself rather than in external storage, so avoiding some store read and write cycles and speeding computation. Also, the use of a 16-bit word to encode the op. code of each instruction enables a much richer and more numerous instruction set to be provided, together with many more addressing modes. The address bus comprises 23 lines, so that a total of 8 megawords or 16 megabytes of program and data storage can be attached to the CPU chip and addressed directly. This is 256 times more than can be attached to the 6800 and more than is normally needed by any single program. The 68000 is well suited to multi-user systems in which a number of users each have access to the system for a brief period in turn.

A crucial requirement for this is that some protection must be provided to ensure that a mistake by one user cannot cause his program to overwrite and so crash another user's program. The 68000 affords this by having two operating modes, User and Supervisor, each of which has its own stack and stack pointer.

Normal application programs are run in user mode, in which the program is not allowed to stray outside prescribed boundaries. Input/output operations and interrupt servicing can be performed only in supervisor mode, so preventing more than one user from trying to access the same peripheral at the same time. The supervisor mode, usually reserved for the operating system, is allowed to use all of the instructions; the user mode cannot execute certain of them and an error is signalled if they are encountered in a program.

Another way in which the 68000 differs from 8-bit microprocessors is that it is a 'two address' machine. This means that there is room in the instruction op. code word to specify both a source and a destination for data. We can thus in a single instruction add together two items held in the data store and leave the result in place of one of them. We can also move data directly from one store location to another. The provision of two address instructions reduces the program size needed for a given task and also reduces its execution time.

In an 8-bit 'single address' machine we need two instructions for each of these tasks since, when adding, one operand must first be loaded into an accumulator, and we can move data from one location to another only via an accumulator.

Having a 16-bit op. code word, the 68000 can encode 12 different address modes for operands; together with 56 instructions and up to three data sizes there are in all over 1000 different instruction codes available. With this degree of complexity, it is quite impractical to plan on converting more than a few instructions from assembly language to machine code by hand, and an assembler is an essential factor in the preparation of any significant program.

## 11.2   Data Types

Many of the instructions of the 68000 can operate on three different data sizes

| | |
|---|---|
| Byte | 8 bits |
| Word | 16 bits |
| Long Word | 32 bits |

For convenience, the same assembler mnemonic is used with all three and the operand size is denoted by adding .B .W or .L to the mnemonic. Thus, to negate a number, we use the mnemonics

| | |
|---|---|
| NEG. B | for a byte |
| NEG. W | for a word |
| NEG. L | for a long word |

There is a decimal add instruction which handles binary-coded decimal numbers and some bit testing and modifying instructions which operate on individual bits.

The data may be coded in four different forms, three of which require symbols to differentiate between them:

% indicates a binary number, as in %10011101.

A decimal integer is written without a prefix, as in 13146.

$ indicates a hexadecimal integer, as in $1A5C.

' as prefix and suffix indicates a character, as in 'B'.

Some assemblers use " or / as in "B" of /B/. A similar notation is used for character strings, as in 'ABCD', etc.

There are restrictions on the characters that can be used in each format; only 0 and 1 can be used in binary, only integers 0-9 in decimal, and only 0-9 and A-F in hexadecimal. Some assemblers require the first hexadecimal character to be a digit, so that $A5C should be input as $0A5C. The characters that can be used are those in the ASCII character set.

## 11.3   CPU Registers

The registers available to the programmer are:

8   32-bit data registers — D0 to D7
7   32-bit address registers — A0 to A6
2   32-bit stack pointers A7 (user) and A7′ (supervisor)
1   32-bit program counter
1   16-bit status register

In the data registers, a byte is stored in bits 0-7, a word in bits 0-15 and a long word in bits 0-31. When fewer than 32 bits are written into a register, the remaining bits are unaltered. Thus writing a byte will load new data into bits 0-7 but will not change bits 8-31. User programs cannot access the supervisor stack pointer, but in supervisor mode both stack pointers are accessible.

In the status register, bits 0-4 comprise the condition code register and bits 8, 9, 10, 13 and 15 are used by the supervisor.

## 11.4   68000 Instructions

Instructions for the 68000 comprise from one to five words, the first always containing the operation code. The following words contain operand addresses in either short or long form. Many single address instructions such as Clear, Increment, Decrement and Negate act in the same way as 6800 instructions, and have a similar format in assembly language. Two address instructions, however, may specify two locations in the external store, identified as source and destination. They are written in this order, so that an instruction which moves a word from register D3 to register D4 would be written as

MOV. W      D3, D4

In an add instruction the two addresses specify the locations of the operands, but the resulting sum is loaded back into the destination. Thus an instruction which adds the word at location NUM1 to the word at NUM2 and puts the sum into location NUM2 would be written as

ADD. W      NUM1, NUM2

The simplest instructions act on a single operand, and include arithmetic, branch and rotate/shift operations. The arithmetic operations are shown in the following list:

| Mnemonic | Action |
|----------|--------|
| CLR. X | Clears data to zero |
| EXT. X | Sign extend |
| NBCD. B | Negate BCD byte with extend |
| NEG. X | Negate |
| NEGX. X | Negate with extend |
| NOT. X | Logical NOT (1's complement) |
| PEA. L | Push effective address onto Stack |
| Scc. B | Set byte if condition code cc is true |
| STOP | Stop CPU with CCR loaded |
| SWAP | Exchange register halves |
| TAS. B | Test and set byte |
| TEST. X | Test operand |

In this list the suffix .X indicates that the operand can be either a byte, a word or a long word.

The sign extend instruction EXT is used when a register has been loaded only partially and the data must be converted into a 32-bit number. The instruction copies the sign bit into all higher-order bits. Thus 01100101 will be changed to

$$00000000000000000000000001100101$$

and 11100101 to

$$11111111111111111111111111100101$$

The negate instruction can be used alone, or as NEGX with sign extend. The Scc instruction uses the same condition mnemonics as the branch instructions, such as NE, EQ, GT, GE etc. in place of cc. The condition code bits are examined and, if the specified condition is satisfied, all bits of the destination operand are set to 1; otherwise all bits are cleared to 0.

The Test and Set instruction tests the operand and sets up the Z and N bits of the condition code register, and then sets bit 7 of the operand byte to 1.

The Test instruction sets up the Z and N bits in accordance with the operand value but does not alter the operand.

## 11.5   Shift and Rotate Instructions

68000 shift and rotate instructions have a family resemblance to those of the 6800, but the availability of two operand codes allows a second operand to specify how many shifts take place, if the data operand is held in one of the data registers. The data size can be 8, 16 or 32 bits. If the data operand is held in the external store, however, only a single bit movement is allowed and only word-size data.

The simplest versions are LSL and LSR, Logical shift left and Logical shift right. In both cases, bits shifted out are routed through the carry bit and zeros are supplied as inputs. The extend bit copies the carry bit. Arithmetic shift left, ASL, is identical to LSL, but Arithmetic shift right copies the sign bit to supply bits at the left-hand end of the data. Output bits are treated as in LSR.

Rotate left, ROL, shifts each bit left and the bit shifted out from the left-hand place is fed into the right-hand place, and also copies into the carry bit. Rotate right, ROR, acts similarly but in the opposite direction. Rotate with extend, ROXL and ROXR, act in the same way, but the bit shifted out is taken via the X bit before being fed into the other end of the register. The various data moves are shown in figure 11.1.

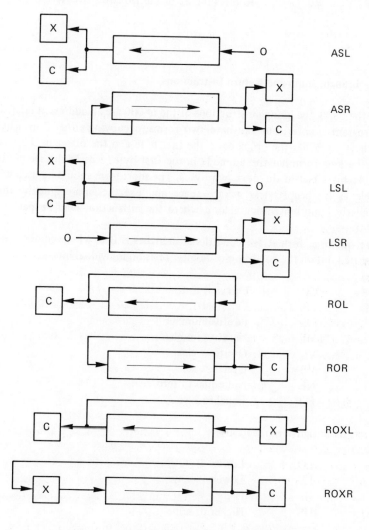

Figure 11.1 68000 shift and rotate instructions.

Examples of shifts are:

| | | |
|---|---|---|
| LSR. L | #5, D4 | Shifts the 32 bits of D4 5 places right |
| LSL. B | D0, D6 | Shifts the LS 8 bits of D6 left *n* bits, where *n* is the number held in D0 |
| LSL. W | NUM1 | Shifts the 16-bit number held in location NUM1 one bit left |

A similar format is used for Rotate instructions, thus:

| | | |
|---|---|---|
| ROL. L | #2, D6 | Rotates the 32 bits in D6 two places left |

## 11.6    Branch, Jump and Return Instructions

As in the 6800, the branch instructions of the 68000 are all addressed relative to the program counter, but can have two forms, occupying either 2 or 4 bytes. The short form has the op. code in the first byte and the offset in the second byte; the long form has the op. code in the first byte, zero in the second byte and a 16-bit offset in the next two bytes. The short form should be used where possible as it occupies less storage space and executes more quickly; this is particularly important inside a loop where the instruction may be performed many times.

The op. code format for conditional branches is Bcc, where cc denotes the test carried out on the condition code bits. Tests on individual bits are:

| | |
|---|---|
| CC | Carry clear |
| CS | Carry set |
| PL | Positive number |
| MI | Negative number |
| VC | Overflow clear |
| VS | Overflow set |
| NE | Not equal to zero |
| EQ | Equal to zero |

Tests on unsigned numbers are:

| | |
|---|---|
| LO | Lower |
| LS | Lower or same |
| HI | Higher |
| HS | Higher or same |

Tests on signed numbers are:

| | |
|---|---|
| LT | Less than |
| LE | Less than or equal to |
| GT | Greater than |
| GE | Greater than or equal |

Most arithmetic and logical operations affect the condition code bits, but if it is necessary to set these bits appropriately without altering any other data, either the Compare or the Test instruction can be used. Compare involves two operands, but Test compares one operand with zero. The compare instruction has four versions:

| | |
|---|---|
| CMP | This subtracts two data items |
| CMPA | This compares two addresses |
| CMPI | This compares a data item with an immediate operand |
| CMPM | This compares two items in external storage |

There is also an unconditional branch instruction **BRA** and a **BSR** (Branch to subroutine).

All of the above have relative addresses; to complete the instruction set there are also similar unconditional branches, but with absolute addresses:

| | |
|---|---|
| JMP | Jump absolute |
| JSR | Jump to subroutine |

Instructions for returning from subroutines of various kinds are:

| | |
|---|---|
| RTE | Return from exception |
| RTR | Return and restore CCR |
| RTS | Return from subroutine |

Some examples are:

| | | |
|---|---|---|
| BEQ. S | LOOP | Branch to the location labelled LOOP if the Z bit is set. This must involve a displacement within the range −128 to +127 bytes; if the displacement is greater than this the instruction must be changed to BEQ. L |
| BCS. S | START | Branch to location START if the carry bit is set |
| BGT. L | TEST | Branch to location TEST if the result of the last operation on the ALU was greater than zero |

**11.7    Addressing Modes**

There are 12 addressing modes available with the 68000. The first seven are distinguished by a 3-bit field in the instruction, and also require a register to be specified in another field. The last five modes do not need to specify a register, so this field can be used to distinguish between these five modes which share the mode code 111. The modes are shown in the following table, together with the syntax used in the assembler and an example.

| Number | Address Mode | Syntax | Example |
|--------|--------------|--------|---------|
| 1 | Data register direct | Dn | D4 |
| 2 | Address register direct | An | A3 |
| 3 | Address register indirect | (An) | (A2) |
| 4 | Address register indirect with post increment | (An) + | (A2) + |
| 5 | Address register indirect with predecrement | -(An) | -(A2) |
| 6 | Address register indirect with 16-bit offset | $d_{16}(An)$ | $67AB(A2) |
| 7 | Address register indirect and indexed with 8-bit offset | $d_8(An,Xn)$ | $4C(A2,A4) |
| 8 | Absolute short | nnnn.W | $4500 |
| 9 | Absolute long | nnnnnnnn.L | $24680135 |
| 10 | Relative to PC with offset | $d_{16}(PC)$ | $4500(PC) |
| 11 | Relative to PC with offset and index | $d_8(PC,Xn)$ | $56(PC,A4) |
| 12 | Immediate | $\#d_8$ | #$5A |
|  |  | $\#d_{16}$ | #$5A43 |
|  |  | $\#d_{32}$ | #$5A436712 |

Modes 4 and 5 are useful for accessing in sequence the items in a block of storage. In mode 4 the register contents are used as the address of the operand and are then incremented. Thus, the initial register contents must be the address of the first item of the block (at the lowest address). Mode 5 will perform the same task, but working in the opposite direction. Thus the initial register contents must point to the data item just below the last item in the block, since the address in this mode is decremented before being used to fetch a data item. In both of these modes the size of the increment is determined by the size of the data item, one for a byte, two for a word or four for a long word.

Two modes provide indexed addressing, 7 and 11. In mode 7 the effective address of the operand is obtained by adding together the contents of the address register, the index register and the 8-bit offset. Mode 11 provides similar addressing, but with the PC instead of the address register, so giving addressing relative to the PC. The effective address is then the sum of the PC, the index register and the offset. Programs which use this address mode can be loaded anywhere in the store and will run correctly, and are said to use 'position independent code'.


## 11.8 Data Move Instructions

All instructions concerned with moving data and addresses are designated as 'MOVE' operations, with additional letters to specify a particular type of move. The options are:

MOVE  Available for all address modes, and all three data lengths. The destination can be a data register or a storage location; the source can be either of these or an address register.

MOVEA  The destination must be an address register but the source can be an address or data register or a storage location. Only word or long word operands are allowed.

MOVEQ  This is available only for loading an immediate 8-bit operand into a data register.

MOVEP  This is available for address modes 1 and 6, and for 16 or 32 bit operands. It is used to move data between a data register and a register in some peripheral interface.

MOVE CCR This version loads the CCR using any address mode but mode 2, with a word length operand.

MOVE SR This moves a word between the Status Register and a data register or a storage location. All address modes are available, except 2, 10, 11, or 12.

MOVE USP This moves a long word between the User Stack Pointer and an address register.

MOVEM  Move Multiple Registers. This is designed to simplify the saving and restoration of register contents when entering and leaving a sub-routine. All address modes apart from 1, 2 and 12 can be used, with word or long word operands. The assembler format must specify which registers are to be moved, and whether they are to be put on the stack or into RAM. The character / is used as a separator between registers with the data registers first, then the address registers. Consecutive registers can be treated as one item; for instance, D3, D4, D5 and D6 can be written as D3–D6. For example:

$$\text{MOVEM.W}\quad \text{D3–D7/A2–A4, –(A7)}$$

saves to the stack the 16-bit words in registers D3, D4, D5, D6, D7, A2, A3, A4. The operation can be reversed by the instruction

$$\text{MOVEM.W}\quad \text{(A7)+, D3–D7/A2–A4}$$

which restores the registers from the stack.

$$\text{MOVEM. L} \quad \text{D2--D5/A3/A5/A6,BLOCK}$$

saves to RAM starting at location BLOCK the registers D2, D3, D4, D5, A3, A5 and A6. The instruction for reversing the operation is

$$\text{MOVEM. L BLOCK, D2--D5/A3/A5/A6}$$

In this case the operands are long words; the instruction copies from the store, starting at location BLOCK into registers D2, D3, D4, D5, A3, A5 and A6.


## 11.9    Arithmetic Operations

Most arithmetic and logical operations involve both a source and a destination and put the result of the operation into the destination, which must thus be a writable location. This requirement restricts the possible address modes since any item in the program (accessed by immediate addressing or addressing relative to the PC) is normally held in ROM and so cannot be changed. These modes are consequently not available to specify destination addresses in the following types of instruction.

The binary addition instruction has the format ADD.X NUM1, NUM2. This adds NUM1 (the source) to NUM2 (the destination) and leaves the sum in the location NUM2. The address modes permitted are as follows:

(1) With a data register as source, the destination can be addressed in any mode except address register direct, relative to the PC or immediate.
(2) With a data register as destination, the source can be addressed in any mode. All three data lengths are allowed.

Exactly the same conditions apply to subtraction instructions of the form SUB.X NUM1, NUM2.

Specific forms of these instructions are:

ADDA and SUBA. These must have an address register as destination but the source can be addressed in any mode. Only word or long word data types are allowed.

ADDI.X and SUBI.X. These can only have immediate source operands but any destination address mode apart from address register direct, relative to PC or immediate.

ADDQ.X and SUBQ.X. These are shorter versions of ADDI and SUBI in which the immediate source operand is limited to three bits. Any destination mode can be used except relative to PC and immediate.

ADDX.X and SUBX.X. These are similar to the ADD and SUB instructions, but also add in the contents of the X bit. This is set equal to the carry bit by arithmetic operations but will not be altered by subsequent MOVE instructions. ADDX.X and SUBX.X can thus be used like ADC and SUBC on the 6800 for multiple word arithmetic. Only two address modes are available:

Source and destination – both data registers (Mode 1)
Source and destination – both address register indirect with pre-decrement
    (Mode 5)

The sign bit of any number held in a data register can be extended by the EXT instruction; EXT.W extends an 8-bit number to 16 bits and EXT.L extends a 16-bit word to 32 bits.

An important feature of the 68000 not found in most 8-bit microprocessors is a hardware multiply and divide facility. This has four instructions which can perform both operations on either signed or unsigned numbers. The destination must be a data register, but the source can be addressed in any mode except address register direct. The MULS and MULU instructions deal with signed and unsigned 16-bit numbers respectively, and leave the 32-bit product in the destination register. The DIVS and DIVU instructions both require a 32-bit number in the destination data register. This is divided by the 16-bit number held in the source and the quotient is left in the destination register (lower half), and the remainder in the upper half. The quotient can be extracted directly by a MOV.W instruction. If the remainder is needed it can be obtained by right shifting the register contents by 16 places, or more quickly by using the SWAP instruction which interchanges the two halves of the register. The remainder will then be in bits 0–15 of the register and can be extracted by a MOV.W operation.

In order to simplify operations on binary coded decimal numbers, three instructions have been included which perform arithmetic in the scale of ten; these provide simpler and more powerful facilities than the single Decimal Add Adjust instruction DAA, available on the 6800.

ABCD adds two BCD numbers and also adds in the X bit. This enables multiple length numbers to be added, but to add the low-order quantities the X bit must initially be cleared. This can be ensured by using the ANDI CCR instruction. The immediate operand here must be a byte which has zero bit 4 (the X bit) and ones elsewhere, and is thus 11101111 or EF. The instruction needed is ANDI CCR #$EF.

ABCD has two possible address modes; both source and destination can either be data registers or locations addressed by mode 5 (address register indirect with predecrement).

Similarly SBCD subtracts two BCD numbers (Destination - Source) but handles only bytes and also subtracts the X bit. It has the same address modes as ABCD.

The third instruction is NBCD which negates a BCD byte and also subtracts the X bit. It can have any address mode apart from address register direct, immediate or relative to the PC.

### 11.10  Logical Operations

The logical instructions available are similar to those provided for the 6800, but they can be used with all three data lengths, and separate versions are needed for immediate operands. Thus the AND.X instruction has two address formats:

Source — Data register, destination — any mode but address register direct, immediate or relative to PC.
Destination — Data register, source — any mode but address register direct.

The exclusive-OR instruction EOR.X can have only a data register for source, but the destination can be addressed by any mode but address register direct, immediate or relative to PC.

The NOT.X instruction has only a destination operand, which can have the same address modes as for EOR.X.

The OR.X instruction has two address formats:

Source — Data register, destination — any mode but data or address register direct, immediate or relative to PC.
Destination — Data register, source — any mode but address register direct.

There are corresponding versions which can have only immediate source operands, namely ANDI.X EORI.X and ORI.X; these can have any destination address mode except address register direct, immediate or relative to the PC. There are specific forms of these which can operate on the status register or on the lower half of it, the condition code register. The operand length must match the register length, so that operations on the SR are word length and those on the CCR are byte length. The instructions thus have op. codes:

| | |
|---|---|
| ANDI.B CCR | ANDI.W SR |
| EORI.B CCR | EORI.W SR |
| ORI.B CCR | ORI.W SR |

The source is an immediate operand and the destination is the CCR or the SR, and the instructions allow the user to set, clear or complement any bit in the CCR or SR.

In this chapter we have examined the basic instruction set of the 68000 and the various address modes available. In the next chapter we give some examples of using the instructions to perform the more common tasks needed for many microprocessor applications.

# 12 Programming the 68000

## 12.1 Arithmetic Operations

The 68000 instruction set provides instructions for performing addition, subtraction and negation with three data sizes. The resolution obtained will be

| | |
|---|---|
| 8-bit data | 1 part in 256 |
| 16-bit data | 1 part in 65 536 |
| 32-bit data | 1 part in over $4 \times 10^9$ |

Although the 8-bit operations rarely provide sufficient resolution, there are few industrial applications where 16-bit resolution is inadequate, since only digital measurements of input quantities can approach this accuracy; analogue measurements are normally much less accurate. For many purposes, word length arithmetic will thus suffice. Where greater accuracy is needed, the full 32-bit operations can be used, but the execution time will be increased by a factor of 1.5 to 2 compared with 16-bit operations. Because the 68000 is a 16-bit device, no time is saved by using 8 bits rather than 16.

In order to cater for the widest range of applications, however, the 68000 does provide for multiple-length operations by means of the X bit whose function resembles that of the C bit in the 6800. Thus, if we require 64-bit addition we can use an ADD.L instruction for the low halves of the numbers and ADDX.L for the high halves.

Therefore, if we wish to add a 64-bit number held in the store in locations NUMH (high-order half) and NUML (low-order half) to another 64-bit number held in D2 (high half) and D3 (low half), the instructions are

| | | |
|---|---|---|
| ADD.L | NUML, D3 | adds low halves |
| ADDX.L | NUMH, D2 | adds high halves and carry bit |

The result is left in registers D2 and D3.

## 12.2 BCD Addition

Unless we are dealing with quite small numbers, the single-byte BCD instructions will not cope with the data sizes likely to be encountered and multiple-byte arithmetic will be required. Program P12.1 shows how 16-bit BCD numbers can be added. It is not a comprehensive version and there is no provision for checking whether overflow has occurred. The numbers are stored in D0 and D1 and the result is left in D1. As we can deal only with a byte at a time, the numbers A and B are labelled:

AL – low byte – in D0 bits 0–7
AH – high byte – in D0 bits 8–15
BL – low byte – in D1 bits 0–7
BH – high byte – in D1 bits 8–15

### *P12.1: BCD Addition*

| Instruction | | Comment |
|---|---|---|
| MOVE.W | D0, D2 | Copy AH and AL into D2 |
| MOVE.W | D1, D3 | Copy BH and BL into D3 |
| LSR | #8, D2 | Shift high byte AH down 8 places |
| LSR | #8, D3 | Shift high byte BH down 8 places |
| ADDI.B | #0, D2 | Add zero to D2 to clear X bit |
| ABCD | D0, D1 | Add low bytes AL and BL |
| ABCD | D2, D3 | Add high bytes AH and BH |
| LSL | #8, D3 | Shift sum (high byte) left 8 places |
| ANDI.W | #$00FF, D1 | Clear bits 8–15 of D1 for high byte of sum |
| ADD.W | D3, D1 | Add high byte of sum to low byte to give 16-bit sum in D1 |

The low bytes can be added directly, but as BCD arithmetic operates only on bits 0–7 of a data register we must shift the high bytes of A and B 8 places right so that they can be added, and then shift the sum 8 places left to position it correctly for combining with the low byte of the sum.

## 12.3 Block Addition

The task of adding together a number of items loaded into successive bytes in the store is somewhat simpler with the 68000 than with earlier microprocessors, since we can use any of the address registers as index registers, and there is no need to increment them after use as the auto-increment address mode will do this automatically. Furthermore, should we require the mean of the numbers, the hardware divider built into the chip makes this a fast and simple operation. As an example, program 12.2 calculates the average of a block of numbers which have previously been loaded into the store starting at the address BLOCK. The number of bytes N is held in register D1 and the address BLOCK in register A0. Before starting the addition loop, the number N is copied into D2 for the later division instruction and D0 is cleared to accumulate the running total.

### *P12:2: Block Addition and Average Program*

| Instruction | Comment |
|---|---|
| CLR.L   D0 | Clear D0 for running total |
| MOVE. L D1, D2 | Copy N (the byte count) to D2 |
| SUBQ. W #1, D1 | Decrement D1 |
| LOOP:  ADD. B   (A0) +, D0 | Add next byte to D0 |
| BCC. S   DECR | Branch to DECR if no Carry |
| ADDI. L   #$100, D0 | Add Carry into D0 |
| DECR:  DBRA   D1, LOOP | Decrement byte count and branch to LOOP if count is not zero |
| DIVS   D1, D0 | Divide sum by N for average |
| ANDI. L   #$0000FFFF, D0 | Mask out remainder, leaving average in D0 |

A simple test with numbers 55, 66, 77 and 88 gives an average of 6E. This is not a rounded-off result as the remainder is rejected. A more accurate result could be obtained by adding N/2 to the total before dividing by N, thus giving a properly rounded-off result.

Where there is a carry from the addition of a byte, it must be added into bit 8 of D0; this is equivalent to the arithmetic addition of 100 (hexadecimal). The loop control is simplified here by using the DBcc instruction. Here cc denotes any one of the conditions which can be used in branch instructions, such as NE, EQ, GT or LE. The instruction tests the condition code bits, and if the condition is satisfied the loop ends. If not, the specified register is decremented and if the count has fallen to −1 the loop ends. Otherwise, the program will branch back to the label which is the second operand in the instructions. In this case we must use the second option by arranging that the initial value of the count in D1 is one less than the number of bytes. We could use the value N directly if we inserted an extra TST.W D1 into the program; this would set the condition code bits according to the contents of D1 and the instruction DBEQ D1, LOOP could be used. Without this the condition code bits will be set according to the result of the previous add instruction, rather than by the state of D1 as we require. To shorten the loop we can omit the Test instruction and insert an extra instruction to decrement the counter, after taking a copy of N in D2. Since the 68000 has neither increment nor decrement instructions, a subtract immediate instruction is used.

The restrictions imposed by this program are that the data items can occupy only one byte, the sum only one long word and the number N only one word. We rarely need provision for a larger sum or more data items, but we may often need more than 8 bits to handle the data if, for example, we are dealing with a set of samples taken from a digital-to-analogue converter which has a resolution of more than 8 bits. The addition must then use word length operations; the same address mode can be used since the address register will automatically be incremented by two, according to the data length of the add instruction. The address BLOCK must, however, be an even number, as words can be addressed only at even locations.

## 12.4 Decimal-to-Binary Conversion

Many digital inputs to a microprocessor are inserted manually from a keyboard or electrically from an instrument such as a digital voltmeter or a frequency meter which gives a decimal display and also electrical signals in decimal code. The code is almost invariably BCD and, as decimal arithmetic in the microprocessor is slow and limited, the first action on the data is usually a conversion to binary notation. Program P12.3 deals with a four-digit number loaded into register D0 (bits 0–15) and leaves the binary equivalent in D2.

The program steps are

Clear D2 for storing the result
Copy BCD number into D1
Mask off bits 0–3 containing the unit's digit
Add this into D2
Shift D0 four places right and copy into D1
Mask off bits 0–3 containing the ten's digit
Multiply by 10 and add into D2
Shift D0 four places right and copy into D1
Mask off bits 0–3 containing the hundred's digit
Multiply by 100 and add into D2
Shift D0 four places right and mask off bits 0–3 containing the thousand's digit
Multiply by 1000 and add into D2, which now contains the binary result

*P12.3: Decimal-to-Binary Conversion Program*

| Instruction | | Comment |
|---|---|---|
| CLR. L | D2 | Clear D2 for result |
| MOVE. L | D0, D1 | Copy number into D1 |
| ANDI. W | #$0F, D1 | Mask off unit's digit |
| ADD. W | D1, D2 | Add it into D2 |
| LSR. W | #4, D0 | Shift number 4 places right |
| MOVE. W | D0, D1 | Copy it into D1 |
| ANDI. W | #$0F, D1 | Mask off ten's digit |
| MULU | #10, D1 | Multiply it by 10 |
| ADD. W | D1, D2 | Add this into D2 |
| LSR. W | #4, D0 | Shift number 4 places right |
| MOVE. W | D0, D1 | Copy it into D1 |
| ANDI. W | #$0F, D1 | Mask off hundred's digit |

| MULU | #100, D1 | Multiply it by 100 |
| ADD.W | D1, D2 | Add this into D2 |
| LSR.W | #4, D0 | Shift number 4 places right |
| MULU | #1000, D0 | Multiply by 1000 |
| ADD.W | D0, D2 | Add MS digit × 1000 into D2 to give the result |

As the last shift right leaves only the thousand's digit in D0, there is no need to mask out unwanted digits before multiplying by 1000. A test run with input 4567 gives the output 11D7, and the maximum input of 9999 converts to 270F.

## 12.5    Binary-to-Decimal Conversion

Where the results of a calculation of data input are to be displayed or printed, it is necessary to convert the internal binary representation into decimal form. Program P12.4 illustrates one way of doing this, using the divide instruction. As in the previous program, the multiply/divide hardware in the 68000 simplifies the procedure considerably. The program starts with the number to be converted in register D0 and gives the decimal equivalent in D1. The number is divided successively by 1000, 100 and 10 (decimal). After each operation the quotient is left in the lower half of D2 and is transferred to D1. It is then shifted 4 places left. The remainder is obtained by a SWAP operation on D2 which moves the remainder from the high half to the low half. This is divided again and the same procedure followed. After three divisions and shifts, the decimal digits are stored in D1 as follows:

| Bits 12-15 | Bits 8-11 | Bits 4-7 | Bits 0-3 |
| Thousand's | Hundred's | Ten's | Unit's |

The final SWAP puts the last remainder, the unit's digit, in bits 0-3 of D2 and it is added into bits 0-3 of D1 to give the result. The program is a skeleton version only; it handles unsigned numbers and to avoid overflow errors it should be preceded by a check on the size of the input. As it caters only for four-digit numbers, the maximum input is 270F which gives an output of 9999. The program performs the reverse operation to that of section 12.4 above, and so an input of 11D7 gives an output of 4567.

### *P12.4: Binary-to-Decimal Conversion*

| Instruction | | Comment |
|---|---|---|
| CLR. L | D1 | Clear D1 for result |
| MOVE. L | D0, D2 | Copy input into D2 |
| DIVU | #1000, D2 | Divide by 1000 |
| MOVE. B | D2, D1 | Copy quotient into D1 |
| LSL. L | #4, D1 | Move it 4 places left |
| SWAP | D2 | Get remainder into LS half of D2 |
| ANDI. L | #$0FFFF, D2 | Mask off remainder |
| DIVU | #100, D2 | Divide it by 100 |
| ADD. B | D2, D1 | Add quotient into D1 |
| LSL. L | #4, D1 | Shift contents of D1 4 places left |
| SWAP | D2 | Get remainder into LS half of D2 |
| ANDI. L | #$0FFFF, D2 | Mask off remainder |
| DIVU | #10, D2 | Divide it by 10 |
| ADD. B | D2, D1 | Add quotient into D1 |
| LSL. L | #4, D1 | Shift contents of D1 4 places left |
| SWAP | D2 | Get remainder into LS half of D2 |
| ADD. B | D2, D1 | Add into D1 to give result |

## 12.6 Subroutines

Subroutines can be used in 68000 programs in the same way as in the 6800; the main program needs a JSR (Jump to subroutine) instruction to transfer control from the main program to the subroutine, and the subroutine must end with an RTS (Return from subroutine) instruction. The JSR instruction, however, can be addressed in many more modes with the 68000. Some modes are not applicable; for example, the subroutine will generally be invoked several times and the same starting address must be loaded into the PC each time. This means that indexed addressing with post-increment or pre-decrement cannot be used, since these will access a different address each time. Also, address register direct and data register direct are not allowed; nor is immediate addressing. As addressing relative to the PC is available, we can write position-independent code, which can be loaded anywhere in the store and will run without alteration.

One of the important requirements in subroutine use is a means of transferring parameters between the main program and the subroutine. This can be done by using the stack, but it is more convenient to use the data registers. These have a total capacity of 32 bytes, so that we have more storage available than is normally needed. In addition to space for passing parameters, we may need some data registers for holding intermediate results. If these contain data needed in the main program we shall have to save their contents at the beginning of the subroutine and then restore them at the end, immediately before the final RTS. The layout of the subroutine then becomes:

| *Main program* | | *Subroutine* |
|---|---|---|
| . . . . . . . . . | SUB: | Save registers needed in subroutine |
| JSR    SUB | | Subroutine processing |
| . . . . . . . . . | | Restore registers |
| | | Return from subroutine |

If, for example, we need to use D3, D4 and A6 for processing in the sub-routine and these are not used to transfer parameters, the subroutine becomes:

| *Instruction* | *Comment* |
|---|---|
| SUB:  MOVEM. L D3/D4/A6, –(A7) | Copy D3, D4 and A6 onto stack |
| . . . . . . . . . . . . | |
| Subroutine body | |
| . . . . . . . . . . . . | |
| MOVEM. L (A7) +, D3/D4/A6 | Restore D3, D4 and A6 from stack |
| RTS | Return from subroutine |

The multiple move instruction is convenient here to move all the registers necessary to and from the stack in one instruction.

The only register which is saved by the processor automatically is the program counter and this is also restored by the RTS instruction. In some situations it is necessary to save and restore also the contents of the condition code register. The contents can be saved by copying the status register onto the stack. This must be done before saving other registers. The return instruction RTR (Restore CCR and return) will then pull the former status register contents off the stack and load the five least significant bits of it into the CCR. It will then pull 32 bits from the stack (the return address) and load them into the PC. The above subroutine will then read:

| *Instruction* | *Comment* |
|---|---|
| SUB:  MOVE. W SR, –(A7) | Copy status register to stack |
| MOVEM. L D3/D4/A6, –(A7) | Copy D3, D4, A6 to stack |
| . . . . . . . . . . . . | |
| Subroutine body | |
| . . . . . . . . . . . . | |
| MOVEM. L (A7) +, D3/D4/A6 | Restore D3, D4, A6 from stack |
| RTR | Restore CCR and return from subroutine |

A simple subroutine which needs only one register to pass a parameter (the time delay required) between the main program and the subroutine is given below. We assume that the lower registers are used in the main program and their contents must be retained, so the highest data register D7 is used for the delay parameter. The main program must load D7 and then jump to the subroutine, which decrements the delay count and returns to the main program when it reaches $-1$.

| *Main program* | *Comment* |
|---|---|
| MOVE.W #XXXX, D7 | Load D7 |
| JSR DELAY | Jump to subroutine DELAY |
| . . . . . . . . . | |

| *Subroutine* | *Comment* |
|---|---|
| DELAY: DBRA D7, DELAY | Decrement D7 until count = $-1$ |
| RTS | Return to main program |

The clock cycles needed for the various instructions are:

| | |
|---|---|
| MOVE.W | 8 |
| JSR | 18 |
| DBRA | 10 (14 for ending loop) |
| RTS | 16 |

If the count loaded into D7 (XXXX) is N, the delay within the loop will be $10(N + 1)$ cycles and the total delay will be this, plus

8 cycles for loading D7
18 cycles for JSR
14 cycles for ending the loop
16 cycles for RTS

The total delay is thus $10(N + 1) + 56$ cycles.

If the microprocessor has an 8 MHz clock rate and there are no extra cycles required waiting for slow storage chips to respond, the count needed for a hundredth of a second will be given by

$$80\,000 = 10(N + 1) + 56$$

since 8 000 000 cycles occur in one second. Thus N = 7993 (decimal).

It is customary to include a 'debouncing' delay after sensing the depression of a key on a keyboard to ensure that the mechanical bouncing of the key contacts will have ended before the key contacts are scanned again. The delay is typically 7–10 milliseconds, so that a count of 6000–8000 would be appropriate in the above subroutine.

### 12.7    Interrupts

The 68000 microprocessor has a powerful and fast mechanism for handling interrupts. Any external device can request an interrupt by signalling along three input lines its priority level. There are seven of these as the eighth state (000) denotes normal working without interrupt. The highest level (111) is not maskable, but all others can be masked. Bits 8, 9 and 10 of the Status Register contain an interrupt mask which can be loaded when the processor is in super-visor mode. When an interrupt is requested, the processor compares the interrupt level with the interrupt mask; only if it is greater than the mask will the interrupt be processed.

If the interrupt is accepted, the processor begins the sequence at the end of the current instruction. The three output lines which indicate the type of action that the processor is performing are set to 111 to denote interrupt acknowledge and the status register is saved in a temporary register. The supervisor bit (bit 13) of the status register is set, so putting the processor into the supervisor mode and the trace bit (bit 15) is cleared so that the processor cannot operate in single shot mode. The interrupt mask is changed to equal the level of the interrupt, so that only a device having higher priority can interrupt the service routine. The external device then puts its vector number on data lines D0–D7, and the PC is pushed onto the supervisor stack followed by the status register. A look-up table in the processor then gives the address from which four bytes are read to give the new contents of the PC. This is the starting address of the service routine which the processor now executes.

The procedure differs from that of the 6800 in that no registers other than the PC and status register are saved. The programmer must save and restore what registers are needed for interrupt servicing at the start and end of the routine. This is conveniently done using the MOVEM instruction in which all registers needed can be saved or restored in one instruction, as explained in section 12.6. The service routine must end with the RTE (Return from exception) instruction, but its format is otherwise similar to that of a subroutine as described in the previous section.

Externally generated interrupts are part of a set of operations called excep-tions which are all treated in a broadly similar manner. Others include a set of TRAP #N instructions which are software interrupts which usually invoke parts of the operating system. Others signify errors, such as attempting to divide by zero, attempting to execute a privilege instruction when in user mode, or address-ing non-existent storage.

An exception which is important for multi-user operation of the 68000 is the CHK (Check) instruction. This allows the program to check whether the contents of any address register are less than zero or greater than the source operand. The main use of the instruction is to prevent one user program from corrupting another, by checking the addresses used to load and store data.

## 12.8 Software for Program Generation

As in the case of 8-bit microprocessors, a number of assemblers are available for the 68000. These are similar to those provided for smaller devices but generally have more facilities, since they will be used to develop more complex software for applications requiring 16-bit microprocessors. In order to develop applications programs quickly and easily a suite of programs is required, usually supplied on one tape or disc. These include:

(1) Editor. This enables programs to be typed in, edited and altered and stored on disc.

(2) Assembler. This takes the output of the Editor (the source program) and checks the syntax. If all the statements correspond to permissible mnemonics they are converted into machine code instructions. This output can be directed to the monitor, the printer or to the disc for subsequent testing. For the first attempt at assembly it is usually quicker to omit machine code output. The assembler will then display only error messages and the lines which caused them. It is then necessary to revert to the Editor to correct the faulty lines and try a further assembly. Only when no errors are indicated is it worth obtaining a machine code output.

(3) Monitor (also called Debugger). This allows a machine code program to be loaded and run, an instruction at a time. After each instruction the contents of all registers and the program store in the neighbourhood of the PC address are displayed. Any of these can be changed before stepping onto the next instruction. Also, breakpoints can be set so that the program will run at full speed until arriving at the breakpoint, when it can be single stepped.

(4) Linker. This program is needed when some program segments and subroutines are held on backing store and are to be incorporated into a source program. It will allocate storage areas for the various parts of the program and adjust the addresses so that the program works as a cohesive whole. The source program must be assembled as position-independent code, which will run correctly wherever it is loaded into the store. It is generated with addresses starting at zero which are changed by the monitor program or by the linker when it is loaded into the store.

## 12.9 Features of 68000 Assemblers

Most 68000 assemblers allow position-dependent code (which must be loaded at a particular place in the store) to be generated. This is essential for programs which will subsequently be held in ROM. The starting address can be specified using the ORG instruction. Thus the command

ORG    $1000

will produce machine code which loads into the store at locations 1000 (hexa-decimal) onwards.

The format of each instruction is

> Label　　　　Op. Code　　　　Operands　　　　Comment

The separator between fields is one or more spaces or a Tab. Thus it is important not to put a space between the operands, otherwise they will be treated as two fields. The only separator allowed between operands is a comma. Program documentation is improved if a brief account of its function is given, together with a title before the assembly language instructions. For this, the entire program line can be devoted to a comment if the * symbol is entered into the first column.

ORG is a mnemonic which falls into the category of assembler directives or pseudo-operations. These do not give rise to machine code instructions but give directions to the assembler. Others are:

END This signifies that there is no more text of the source code to be examined. It must always be the last line of the source program, but it is not essential for all assemblers.

DC Define constant. This enables storage to be reserved, labelled and given initial values. For example, the line

> DATA　　　　　　　DC.B　　　　　　　　　　10,20,30

loads three bytes with the constants 10, 20 and 30. They can be referred to as

> DATA　　　which has the value　　10
> DATA+1　　which has the value　　20
> DATA+2　　which has the value　　30

DS Define space. This operates in a similar manner to DC but the constants indicate the number of items to be reserved. Some assemblers initially set the contents to zero. The line

> SAMPL　　　　　　　DS.W　　　　　　　　　　20

will reserve a block of 20 words of storage, the first of which has the address SAMPL.

Conditional assembly can be specified by a statement such as

> IFEQ　　　　NUM

where NUM may be a variable or an expression. It is evaluated and compared with zero, and if equal the following statements are assembled. If not equal to zero, assembly is suspended until reaching the ENDC statement, and starts again with the next statement. Other conditions can be imposed using the mnemonics

|       |     |      |     |
|-------|-----|------|-----|
| IFNE  | NUM | IFGE | NUM |
| IFGE  | NUM | IFLT | NUM |
| IFLE  | NUM |      |     |

Macros can be defined as follows

| MAC1 | MACRO | |
|------|-------|---|
|      | . . . . . . . | Body of Macro |
|      | . . . . . . . | |
|      | ENDM  | |

This would be invoked by the call

MAC1

## 12.10 Examples of Assembler Output

Most 68000 assemblers are larger and more comprehensive than those for 8-bit microprocessors, and so there are many more error messages which can give more specific details of the mistakes found by the assembler. The following program has several errors. The assembler numbers each line of the program and uses these to refer to the errors. To clarify the print-out, comments and leading zeros in the addresses have been omitted.

| *Line No.* | *Location* | *Code* | | | *Instruction* | |
|------------|------------|--------|---|---|---------------|---|
| 1 | | | | *** | ERROR TEST | |
| 2 | | | | *** | TITLE TEST1 | |
| Error 1 | unrecognised instruction at line 3 | | | | | |
| 3 | | | | | CLS.L | D1 |
| 4 | 00 | 4280 | | | CLR.L | D0 |
| 5 | 02 | 2803 | | LAB1 | MOVE.L | D3,D4 |
| Error 2 | undefined label at line 6 | | | | | |
| 6 | 04 | 23C500000000 | | | MOVE.L | D5, D6 |
| Error 5 | phasing error at line 7 | | | | | |
| 7 | | | | LAB1 | ADD.C | D2,D3 |
| Error 12 | data too large at line 8 | | | | | |
| 8 | 0A | 103C0059 | | | MOVE.B | #345,D0 |
| Error 2 | undefined label at line 9 | | | | | |
| 9 | 0E | 207C00000000B00000000 | | | MOVEA.L | #123,A9 |
| | | | | | END | |

The first error is using an instruction CLS which is allowed in **BASIC** but is not a valid 68000 mnemonic. The first occurrence of the label LAB1 is accepted, but the second occurrence in line 7 cannot be correct and the term 'phasing error' includes labels defined twice. The op. code is wrong as the data size (C) is illegal. Line 6 has a space between D5 and D6 which causes the assembler to treat them as separate fields. In line 8 the operand 345 is too large to store in one byte. Finally, in line 9 as A9 is not a valid register it is taken as an address label. However, it is not given a value, so the assembler cannot generate the address part of the instruction. All of these errors must be removed by altering the source program before the assembler output will run correctly.

In the remainder of this section we give the assembled versions of some of the programs discussed in previous sections, starting with the BCD addition program. In order to enter some test data two instructions are added to load the numbers 1234 and 4567 into D0 and D1.

To allow for the comments, the line numbers allocated by the assembler have been omitted.

### P12.1a: BCD Addition

| Location | Code | Instruction | | Comment |
|----------|------|-------------|---|---------|
| | | **\*\*TITLE: BCDADD** | | |
| 00 | 203C00001234 | MOVE.L | #$1234,D0 | Load 1234 into D0 |
| 06 | 223C00004567 | MOVE.L | #$4567,D1 | Load 4567 into D1 |
| 0C | 3400 | MOVE.W | D0,D2 | Copy AH and AL into D2 |
| 0E | 3601 | MOVE.W | D1,D3 | Copy BH and BL into D3 |
| 10 | E08A | LSR.L | #8,D2 | Shift high byte AH 8 places |
| 12 | E088 | LSR.L | #8,D3 | Shift high byte BH 8 places |
| 14 | C300 | ABCD | D0,D1 | Add low bytes AL and BL |
| 16 | C702 | ABCD | D2,D3 | Add high bytes AH and BH |
| 18 | E14B | LSL.L | #8,D3 | Shift sum left 8 8 places |
| 1A | 0281000000FF | ANDI.L | #$0FF,D1 | Clear bits 8–15 of D1 for high byte of sum |
| 20 | D283 | ADD.L | D3,D1 | Add high byte of sum to low byte |
| | | END | | to give 16-bit sum in D1 |

The addresses which start from 00 have had leading zeros removed to save space. With the data given, the result is 5801 in D1 as expected.

### P12.2a: Block Addition and Average Program

| Location | Code | Instruction | | Comment |
|---|---|---|---|---|
| | | ** *TITLE: BLKADD* | | |
| 00 | 207C00004000 | MOVEA.L | #$4000,A0 | Load starting address |
| 06 | 223C00000004 | MOVE.L | #$4,D1 | Load byte count |
| 0C | 4280 | CLR.L | D0 | Clear D0 for sum |
| 0E | 2401 | MOVE.L | D1,D2 | Copy byte count to D2 |
| 10 | 5341 | SUBQ.W | #1,D1 | Decrement D1 |
| 12 | D018 | LOOP: ADD.B | (A0)+,D0 | Add next byte to D0 |
| 14 | 6406 | BCC.S | DECR | Branch to DECR if no carry |
| 16 | 068000000100 | ADDI.L | #$100,D0 | Add carry into D0 |
| 1C | 51C9FFF4 | DECR:DBRA | D1,LOOP | Decrement byte count and branch to LOOP if count is not −1 |
| 20 | 81C2 | DIVS | D2,D0 | Divide sum by byte count for average |
| 22 | 02800000FFFF | ANDI.L END | #$0FFFF,D0 | Mask out remainder, average in D0 |

SYMBOL TABLE

| DECR | 1C | R | LOOP | 12 | R |
|---|---|---|---|---|---|

As with the previous program some extra instructions have been added to load test data. Only four items are used, loaded into locations 4000-4003 (hex). Thus the starting address, 4000, is loaded into A0 and the number of items, 4, is loaded into D1. Two labels are used in the program (LOOP and DECR) so that a symbol table is output showing the addresses allocated to them. They are tagged with R to indicate that they, along with the rest of the program, are relocatable and will be loaded higher in the address space for testing and running.

## P12.3a: Decimal-to-Binary Conversion Program

| Location | Code | Instruction | | Comment |
|---|---|---|---|---|
| | | **\*\*TITLE: DECBIN** | | |
| 00 | 4282 | CLR.L | D2 | Clear D2 for result |
| 02 | 2200 | MOVE.L | D0,D1 | Copy number into D1 |
| 04 | 0241000F | ANDI.W | #$0F | Mask off unit's digit |
| 08 | D441 | ADD.W | D1,D2 | Add it into D2 |
| 0A | E848 | LSR.W | #4,D0 | Shift number 4 places right |
| 0C | 3200 | MOVE.W | D0,D1 | Copy it into D1 |
| 0E | 0241000F | ANDI.B | #$0F,D1 | Mask off ten's digit |
| 12 | C2FC000A | MULU | #10,D1 | Multiply it by 10 |
| 16 | D441 | ADD.W | D1,D2 | Add this into D2 |
| 18 | E848 | LSR.W | #4,D0 | Shift number 4 places right |
| 1A | 3200 | MOVE.W | D0,D1 | Copy it into D1 |
| 1C | 0241000F | ANDI.W | #$0F,D1 | Mask off hundred's digit |
| 20 | C2FC0064 | MULU | #100,D1 | Multiply by 100 |
| 24 | D441 | ADD.W | D1,D2 | Add this into D2 |
| 26 | E848 | LSR.W | #4,D0 | Shift number 4 places left |
| 28 | C0FC03E8 | MULU | #1000,D0 | Multiply by 1000 |
| 2C | D440 | ADD.W | D0,D2 | Add MS digit × 1000 into D2 to give the |
| | | END | | final result |

This program converts a positive 4-digit BCD number held in D0 into a binary number which is loaded into D2. There is no need to test the magnitude of the input number as the largest BCD number which can occur (9999) converts to 270F, which is well within the capacity of a 16-bit register.

The program can be tested using a monitor program to load the BCD number into D0, run the program and examine the contents of D2.

## P12.4a: Binary-to-Decimal Conversion

| Location | Code | Instruction | | Comment |
|---|---|---|---|---|
| | | **\*\*TITLE: BINDEC** | | |
| 00 | 4281 | CLR.L | D1 | Clear D1 for result |
| 02 | 2400 | MOVE.L | D0,D2 | Copy input into D2 |
| 04 | 84FC03E8 | DIVU | #1000,D2 | Divide by 1000 |
| 08 | 1202 | MOVE.B | D2,D1 | Copy quotient into D1 |
| 0A | E989 | LSL.L | #4,D1 | Move it 4 places left |
| 0C | 4842 | SWAP | D2 | Get remainder |
| 0E | 02820000FFFF | ANDI.L | #$0FFFF,D2 | Mask off in LS half of D2 |
| 14 | 84FC0064 | DIVU | #100,D2 | Divide it by 100 |
| 18 | D202 | ADD.B | D2,D1 | Add quotient into D1 |
| 1A | E989 | LSL.L | #4,D1 | Shift D1 4 places left |
| 1C | 4842 | SWAP | D2 | Get remainder |
| 1E | 02820000FFFF | ANDI.L | #$0FFFF,D2 | Mask off in LS half of D2 |
| 24 | 84FC000A | DIVU | #10,D2 | Divide by 10 |
| 28 | D202 | ADD.B | D2,D1 | Add quotient into D1 |
| 2A | E989 | LSL.L | #4,D1 | Shift D1 4 places left |
| 2C | 4842 | SWAP | D2 | Get remainder in LS half |
| 2E | D202 | ADD.B | D2,D1 | Add into D1 for result |
| | | END | | |

This program can also be tested by using a monitor to load the binary input into D0, running the program and observing the output in D1.

# Appendix 1: 6800 Instruction Set

**Store Reference Instructions**

| OPERATION | MNEMONIC | ADDRESS MODES | | | |
|---|---|---|---|---|---|
| | | Immediate | Direct | Indexed | Extended |
| Add to A | ADDA | 8B | 9B | AB | BB |
| Add to B | ADDB | CB | DB | EB | FB |
| Add to A + Carry | ADCA | 89 | 99 | A9 | B9 |
| Add to B + Carry | ADCB | C9 | D9 | E9 | F9 |
| AND with A | ANDA | 84 | 94 | A4 | B4 |
| AND with B | ANDB | C4 | D4 | E4 | F4 |
| Bit test with A | BITA | 85 | 95 | A5 | B5 |
| Bit test with B | BITB | C5 | D5 | E5 | F5 |
| Clear | CLR | | | 6F | 7F |
| Compare with A | CMPA | 81 | 91 | A1 | B1 |
| Compare with B | CMPB | C1 | D1 | E1 | F1 |
| Complement (1's) | COM | | | 63 | 73 |
| Decrement | DEC | | | 6A | 7A |
| Exclus. OR with A | EORA | 88 | 98 | A8 | B8 |
| Exclus. OR with B | EORB | C8 | D8 | E8 | F8 |
| Increment | INC | | | 6C | 7C |
| Load Acc. A | LDAA | 86 | 96 | A6 | B6 |
| Load Acc. B | LDAB | C6 | D6 | E6 | F6 |
| OR with A | ORAA | 8A | 9A | AA | BA |
| OR with B | ORAB | CA | DA | EA | FA |
| Rotate Left | ROL | | | 69 | 79 |
| Rotate Right | ROR | | | 66 | 76 |
| Shift Left, Arith. | ASL | | | 68 | 78 |
| Shift Right, Arith. | ASR | | | 67 | 77 |
| Shift Right, Logic | LSR | | | 64 | 74 |
| Store Acc. A | STAA | | 97 | A7 | B7 |
| Store Acc. B | STAB | | D7 | E7 | F7 |
| Subtract from A | SUBA | 80 | 90 | A0 | B0 |
| Subtract from B | SUBB | C0 | D0 | E0 | F0 |

| | | | | | |
|---|---|---|---|---|---|
| Sub. from A with Carry | SBCA | 82 | 92 | A2 | B2 |
| Sub. from B with Carry | SBCB | C2 | D2 | E2 | F2 |
| Test | TST | | | 6D | 7D |
| Compare Index Reg. | CPX | 8C | 9C | AC | BC |
| Load Index Reg. | LDX | CE | DE | EE | FE |
| Load Stack Pointer | LDS | 8E | 9E | AE | BE |
| Store Index Reg. | STX | | DF | EF | FF |
| Store Stack Pointer | STS | | 9F | AF | BF |

## Implicitly Addressed Instructions

| OPERATION | MNEMONIC | CODE |
|---|---|---|
| Add Accumulators | ABA | 1B |
| Clear Acc. A | CLRA | 4F |
| Clear Acc. B | CLRB | 5F |
| Compare Accumulators | CBA | 11 |
| Complement Acc. A | COMA | 43 |
| Complement Acc. B | COMB | 53 |
| Negate Acc. A | NEGA | 40 |
| Negate Acc. B | NEGB | 50 |
| Decimal Adjust Acc. A | DAA | 19 |
| Decrement Acc. A | DECA | 4A |
| Decrement Acc. B | DECB | 5A |
| Increment Acc. A | INCA | 4C |
| Increment Acc. B | INCB | 5C |
| Push from Acc. A | PSHA | 36 |
| Push from Acc. B | PSHB | 37 |
| Pull to Acc. A | PULA | 32 |
| Pull to Acc. B | PULB | 33 |
| Rotate Left Acc. A | ROLA | 49 |
| Rotate Left Acc. B | ROLB | 59 |
| Arith. Shift Left Acc. A | ASLA | 48 |
| Arith. Shift Left Acc. B | ASLB | 58 |
| Arith. Shift Right Acc. A | ASRA | 47 |
| Arith. Shift Right Acc. B | ASRB | 57 |
| Logic Shift Right Acc. A | LSRA | 44 |
| Logic Shift Right Acc. B | LSRB | 54 |
| Subtract Accumulators | SBA | 10 |
| Transfer Accumulators A to B | TAB | 16 |
| Transfer Accumulators B to A | TBA | 17 |
| Test Acc. A | TSTA | 4D |

| Test Acc. B | TSTB | 5D |
|---|---|---|
| Decrement Index Reg. | DEX | 09 |
| Decrement Stack Pointer | DES | 34 |
| Increment Index Reg. | INX | 08 |
| Increment Stack Pointer | INS | 31 |
| Transfer IR to SP | TXS | 35 |
| Transfer SP to IR | TSX | 31 |
| | | |
| Clear Carry Bit | CLC | 0C |
| Clear Interrupt Mask | CLI | 0E |
| Clear Overflow Bit | CLV | 0A |
| Set Carry Bit | SEC | 0D |
| Set Interrupt Mask | SEI | 0F |
| Set Overflow Bit | SEV | 0B |
| Transfer Acc. A to CC Reg. | TAP | 06 |
| Transfer CC Reg. to Acc. A | TPA | 07 |

## Branch Instructions — Relative Addressing

| OPERATION | MNEMONIC | CODE |
|---|---|---|
| Branch Always | BRA | 20 |
| Branch if Carry Clear | BCC | 24 |
| Branch if Carry Set | BCS | 25 |
| Branch if = Zero | BEQ | 27 |
| Branch if ⩾ Zero | BGE | 2C |
| Branch if > Zero | BGT | 2E |
| Branch if Higher | BHI | 22 |
| Branch if ⩽ Zero | BLE | 2F |
| Branch if Lower or Same | BLS | 23 |
| Branch if Minus | BMI | 2B |
| Branch if Not = Zero | BNE | 26 |
| Branch if Overflow Clear | BVC | 28 |
| Branch if Overflow Set | BVS | 29 |
| Branch if Plus | BPL | 2A |
| Branch to Subroutine | BSR | 8D |

**Jump and Return Instructions**

| | | *ADDRESS MODES* | | |
|---|---|---|---|---|
| *OPERATION* | *MNEMONIC* | *Indexed* | *Extended* | *Implicit* |
| Jump | JMP | 6E | 7E | |
| Jump to Subroutine | JSR | AD | BD | |
| No Operation | NOP | | | 01 |
| Return from Interrupt | RTI | | | 3B |
| Return from Subroutine | RTS | | | 39 |
| Software Interrupt | SWI | | | 3F |
| Wait for Interrupt | WAI | | | 3E |

# Appendix 2: Z80 Instruction Set

## 8-bit Load Operations

SOURCE

| | | A | B | C | D | E | H | L | (HL) | (BC) | (DE) | X | Y | Immed. |
|---|---|---|---|---|---|---|---|---|---|---|---|---|---|---|
| D R **B** | | 7F | 78 | 79 | 7A | 7B | 7C | 7D | 7E | 0A | 1A | DD7E | FD7E | 3E |
| e | | 47 | 40 | 41 | 42 | 43 | 44 | 45 | 46 | | | DD46 | FD46 | 06 |
| E g **C** | | 4F | 48 | 49 | 4A | 4B | 4C | 4D | 4E | | | DD4E | FD4E | 0E |
| i | | | | | | | | | | | | | | |
| S s **D** | | 57 | 50 | 51 | 52 | 53 | 54 | 55 | 56 | | | DD56 | FD56 | 16 |
| t | | | | | | | | | | | | | | |
| T e **E** | | 5F | 58 | 59 | 5A | 5B | 5C | 5D | 5E | | | DD5E | FD5E | 1E |
| r | | | | | | | | | | | | | | |
| I **H** | | 67 | 60 | 61 | 62 | 63 | 64 | 65 | 66 | | | DD66 | DF66 | 26 |
| N **L** | | 6F | 68 | 69 | 6A | 6B | 6C | 6D | 6E | | | DD6E | FD6E | 2E |
| A | | | | | | | | | | | | | | |
| g **(HL)** | | 77 | 70 | 71 | 72 | 73 | 74 | 75 | | | | | | 36 |
| T I **(BC)** | | 02 | | | | | | | | | | | | |
| I n | | | | | | | | | | | | | | |
| d. **(DE)** | | 12 | | | | | | | | | | | | |
| O | | | | | | | | | | | | | | |
| N I **X** | | DD 77 | DD 70 | DD 71 | DD 72 | DD 73 | DD 74 | DD 75 | | | | | | DD 36 |
| n d | | | | | | | | | | | | | | |
| e **Y** | | FD 77 | FD 70 | FD 71 | FD 72 | FD 73 | FD 74 | FD 75 | | | | | | FD 36 |
| x | | | | | | | | | | | | | | |

*Register* spans columns A–L. *Register Indirect* spans (HL) (BC) (DE). *Indexed* spans X Y.

The register instructions have the format LD Rd, Rs where Rd and Rs are the destination and source register respectively. Register Indirect addresses are specified as (IX + d) or (IY + d). The displacement d is held in the third byte. Two instructions allow the accumulator to be loaded from or stored in a 16-bit address nn held in the second and third bytes:

LD A,nn — 3A nn and LD nn, A — 32 nn

To move the contents of the I and R registers to and from the Accumulator there are four instructions:

LD A, I — ED 57     LD I, A — ED 47
LD A, R — ED 5F     LD R, A — ED 4F

## 16-bit Load Operations

| | | | |
|---|---|---|---|
| Register–register | LD SP, HL — F9 | LD SP, IX — DD F9 | |
| | | LD SP, IY — FD F9 | |
| Immediate operand | LD BC, nn — 01 nn | LD DE, nn — 11 nn | |
| LD HL, nn — 21 nn | LD SP, nn — 31 nn | LD IX, nn — DD 21 nn | |
| LD IY, nn — FD 21 nn | | | |
| Absolute address | LD BC, (nn) — ED 48 nn | LD DE,(nn) — ED 58 nn | |
| LD HL, (nn) — 2A nn | LD SP, (nn) — ED 7B nn | LD IX, (nn) — DD 2A nn | |
| LD IY, (nn) — FD 2A nn | LD (nn), BC — ED 43 nn | LD (nn), DE — ED 53 nn | |
| LD (nn), HL — 22 nn | LD (nn), SP — ED 73 nn | LD (nn), IX — DD 22 nn | |
| LD (nn), IY — FD 22 nn | | | |
| Stack operations | PUSH AF — F5 | PUSH BC — C5 | PUSH DE — D5 |
| PUSH HL — E5 | PUSH IX — DD E5 | PUSH IY — FD E5 | POP AF — D1 |
| POP BC — C1 | POP DE — D1 | POP HL — E1 | POP IX — DD E1 |
| POP IY — FD E1 | | | |

## Exchanges

EX AF,AF' — 08     EXX' — D9     EX DE,HL — EB     EX (SP),HL — E3
EX (SP),IX — DD E3     EX (SP),IY — FD E3

## Block Transfers

Load and Increment — LDI — ED A0 — LD (DE), (HL), INC HL and DE, DEC BC.
Load, Increment and Repeat — LDIR — ED B0 — Repeated execution of LDI until BC = 0.
Load and Decrement — LDD — ED A8 — LD (DE), (HL),DEC HL and DE,DEC BC.
Load, Decrement and Repeat — LDDR — ED B8 — Repeated execution of LDD until BC = 0.   Register HL holds source address.
Register DE holds destination address; Register BC is Byte Counter.

**Block Searches**

Four block search instructions operate in a similar manner to the above block transfers. Each item is compared with the contents of the accumulator and the zero flag is set when a match is found. In the repeated operation the search ends when either a match is found or the byte count in register BC falls to zero.

Compare and Increment – CPI – ED A1
Compare, Increment and Repeat – CPIR – ED B1
Compare and Decrement – CPD – ED A9
Compare, Decrement and Repeat – CPDR – ED B9

**Accumulator, Flag, and CPU Operations**

| Decimal Adjust Acc. | DAA | 27 | Complement Acc. | CPL | 2F |
|---|---|---|---|---|---|
| Negate Acc. (2's Comp.) | NEG | ED 44 | Complement Carry Flag | CCF | 3F |
| Set Carry Flag | SCF | 37 | No Operation | NOP | 00 |
| Halt | HALT | 76 | Disable Interrupts | DI | F3 |
| Enable Interrupts | EI | FB | Set Int. Mode 0 | IM0 ED 46 | |
| Set Int. Mode 1 | IM1 | ED 56 | Set Int. Mode 2 | IM2 ED 5E | |

**Restart Group**

| Vector Address | 0000 | 0008 | 0010 | 0018 | 0020 | 0028 | 0030 | 0038 |
|---|---|---|---|---|---|---|---|---|
| Instruction | RST 0 | RST 1 | RST 2 | RST 3 | RST 4 | RST 5 | RST 6 | RST 7 |
| Op. Code | C7 | CF | D7 | DF | E7 | EF | F7 | FF |

## 8-bit Arithmetic and Logic Operations

### *SOURCE*

| | *A* | *B* | *C* | *D* | *E* | *H* | *L* | *Reg. Ind. (HL)* | *IX* | *IY* | *Imm.* |
|---|---|---|---|---|---|---|---|---|---|---|---|
| | | | *Register Addressing* | | | | | | *Indexed* | | |
| ADD | 87 | 80 | 81 | 82 | 83 | 84 | 95 | 86 | DD 86 | FD 86 | C6 |
| ADC | 8F | 88 | 89 | 8A | 8B | 8C | 8D | 8E | DD 8E | FD 8E | CE |
| SUB | 97 | 90 | 91 | 92 | 93 | 94 | 95 | 96 | DD 96 | FD 96 | D6 |
| SBC | 9F | 98 | 99 | 9A | 9B | 9C | 9D | 9E | DD 9E | FD 9E | DE |
| AND | A7 | A0 | A1 | A2 | A3 | A4 | A5 | A6 | DD A6 | FD A6 | E6 |
| XOR | AF | A8 | A9 | AA | AB | AC | AD | AE | DD AE | FD AE | EE |
| OR | B7 | B0 | B1 | B2 | B3 | B4 | B5 | B6 | DD B6 | FD B6 | F6 |
| CP Compare | BF | B8 | B9 | BA | BB | BC | BD | BE | DD BE | FD BE | FE |
| INC Increment | 3C | 04 | 0C | 14 | 1C | 24 | 2C | 34 | DD 34 | FD 34 | – |
| DEC Decrement | 3D | 05 | 0D | 15 | 1D | 25 | 2D | 35 | DD 35 | FD 35 | – |

The third byte of the indexed instructions carries the displacement.
The second byte of the immediate instructions carries the operand.

## 16-bit Operations

*OPERATION*                                    *SOURCE*

| | | | BC | DE | HL | SP | IX | IY |
|---|---|---|---|---|---|---|---|---|
| D E S | ADD | HL | 09 | 19 | 29 | 39 | | |
| T I N | ADD | IX | DD 09 | DD 19 | | DD 39 | DD 29 | |
| A T | ADD | IY | FD 09 | FD 19 | | FD 39 | | FD 29 |
| I O | ADC | HL | ED 4A | ED 5A | ED 6A | ED 7A | | |
| N | SBC | HL | ED 42 | ED 52 | ED 62 | ED 72 | | |
| | Increment | INC | 03 | 13 | 23 | 33 | DD 23 | FD 23 |
| | Decrement | DEC | 0B | 1B | 2B | 3B | DD 2B | FD 2B |

## Rotate and Shift Operations

*OP. CODE*                                    *OPERAND*

| | A | B | C | D | E | H | L | (HL) | (IX+d) | (IY+d) |
|---|---|---|---|---|---|---|---|---|---|---|
| RLC | CB 07 | CB 00 | CB 01 | CB 02 | CB 03 | CB 04 | CB 05 | CB 06 | DD CB d 06 | FD CB d 06 |
| RRC | CB 0F | CB 08 | CB 09 | CB 0A | CB 0B | CB 0C | CB 0D | CB 0E | DD CB d 0E | FD CB d 0E |
| SLA | CB 27 | CB 20 | CB 21 | CB 22 | CB 23 | CB 24 | CB 25 | CB 26 | DD CB d 26 | FD CB d 26 |
| SRA | CB 2F | CB 28 | CB 29 | CB 2A | CB 2B | CB 2C | CB 2D | CB 2E | DD CB d 2E | FD CB d 2E |
| SRL | CB 3F | CB 38 | CB 39 | CB 3A | CB 3B | CB 3C | CB 3D | CB 3E | DD CB d 3E | FD CB d 3E |
| RLD | | | | | | | | ED 6F | | |
| RRD | | | | | | | | ED 67 | | |

RLCA – 07          RRCA – 0F          RLA – 17          RRA – 1F

A diagram of the shift and rotate operations is shown in figure A2.1.

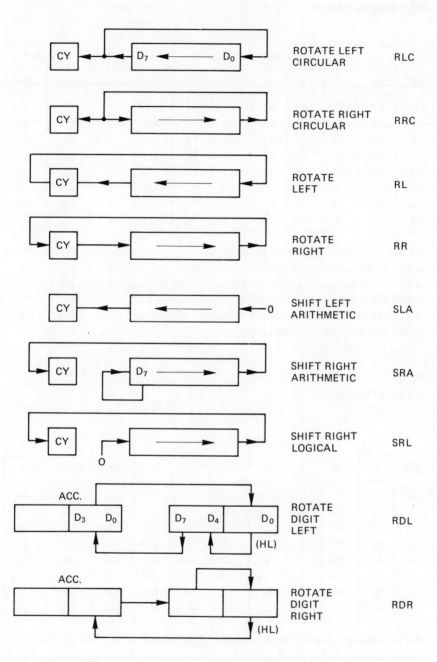

Figure 12.1 Z80 rotate and shift operations.

**Bit-testing Operations**

| | | | Register Addressing | | | | | Reg. Indir. | Indexed | |
|---|---|---|---|---|---|---|---|---|---|---|
| BIT | A | B | C | D | E | H | L | (HL) | (IX+d) | (IY+d) |
| 0 | 47 | 40 | 41 | 42 | 43 | 44 | 45 | 46 | 46 | 46 |
| 1 | 4F | 48 | 49 | 4A | 4B | 4C | 4D | 4E | 4E | 4E |
| 2 | 57 | 50 | 51 | 52 | 53 | 54 | 55 | 56 | 56 | 56 |
| 3 | 5F | 58 | 59 | 5A | 5B | 5C | 5D | 5E | 5E | 5E |
| 4 | 67 | 60 | 61 | 62 | 63 | 64 | 65 | 66 | 66 | 66 |
| 5 | 6F | 68 | 69 | 6A | 6B | 6C | 6D | 6E | 6E | 6E |
| 6 | 77 | 70 | 71 | 72 | 73 | 74 | 75 | 76 | 76 | 78 |
| 7 | 7F | 78 | 79 | 7A | 7B | 7C | 7D | 7E | 7E | 7E |

All Register and Register Indirect Mode instructions have the form CB XX, where XX is the entry in the above table.

All Indexed instructions using the IX register (IX+d) have the form DD CB d XX, where XX is the entry in the table.

All indexed instructions using the IY register (IY+d) have the form FD CB d XX, where XX is the entry in the table.

d is an 8-bit displacement.

**Bit-reset Operations**

| | | | Register Addressing | | | | | Reg. Indir. | Indexed | |
|---|---|---|---|---|---|---|---|---|---|---|
| BIT | A | B | C | D | E | H | L | (HL) | (IX+d) | (IY+d) |
| 0 | 87 | 80 | 81 | 82 | 83 | 84 | 85 | 86 | 86 | 86 |
| 1 | 8F | 88 | 89 | 8A | 8B | 8C | 8D | 8E | 8E | 8E |
| 2 | 97 | 90 | 91 | 92 | 93 | 94 | 95 | 96 | 96 | 96 |
| 3 | 9F | 98 | 99 | 9A | 9B | 9C | 9D | 9E | 9E | 9E |
| 4 | A7 | A0 | A1 | A2 | A3 | A4 | A5 | A6 | A6 | A6 |
| 5 | AF | A8 | A9 | AA | AB | AC | AD | AE | AE | AE |
| 6 | B7 | B0 | B1 | B2 | B3 | B4 | B5 | B6 | B6 | B8 |
| 7 | BF | B8 | B9 | BA | BB | BC | BD | BE | BE | BE |

All Register and Register Indirect Mode instructions have the form CB XX, where XX is the entry in the above table.

All Indexed instructions using the IX register (IX+d) have the form DD CB d XX, where XX is the entry in the table.

All Indexed instructions using the IY register (IY+d) have the form **FD CB** d **XX**, where **XX** is the entry in the table.
d is an 8-bit displacement.

## Bit-setting Operations

| BIT | \multicolumn{7}{c}{Register Addressing} | Reg. Indir. | \multicolumn{2}{c}{Indexed} |
|---|---|---|---|---|---|---|---|---|---|---|
| | *A* | *B* | *C* | *D* | *E* | *H* | *L* | *(HL)* | *(IX+d)* | *(IY+d)* |
| 0 | C7 | C0 | C1 | C2 | C3 | C4 | C5 | C6 | C6 | C6 |
| 1 | CF | C8 | C9 | CA | CB | CC | CD | CE | CE | CE |
| 2 | D7 | D0 | D1 | D2 | D3 | D4 | D5 | D6 | D6 | D6 |
| 3 | DF | D8 | D9 | DA | DB | DC | DD | DE | DE | DE |
| 4 | E7 | E0 | E1 | E2 | E3 | E4 | E5 | E6 | E6 | E6 |
| 5 | EF | E8 | E9 | EA | EB | EC | ED | EE | EE | EE |
| 6 | F7 | F0 | F1 | F2 | F3 | F4 | F5 | F6 | F6 | F8 |
| 7 | FF | F8 | F9 | FA | FB | FC | FD | FE | FE | FE |

All Register and Register Indirect Mode instructions have the form **CB XX**, where **XX** is the entry in the above table.
All Indexed instructions using the IX register (IX+d) have the form **DD CB** d **XX**, where **XX** is the entry in the table.
All Indexed instructions using the IY register (IY+d) have the form **FD CB** d **XX**, where **XX** is the entry in the table.
d is an 8-bit displacement.

# Appendix 3:  6502 Instruction Set

**Address Modes**

1. Immediate (IMM). The operand is in the second byte of the instruction.
2. Absolute (ABS). The operand address is in the second and third bytes of the instruction.
3. Zero Page (ZP). The operand address is in the second byte of the instruction (must be less than 100 hex).
4. Indexed Zero Page (ZP, X). The effective address is the sum of the second byte of the instruction and the contents of the X index register.
5. Indexed Absolute (ABS, X). The effective address is the sum of the 16-bit address in the instruction and the contents of the X index register.
6. Indexed Absolute (ABS, Y). As above but using Y register.
7. Indexed indirect (IND, X). The second byte of the instruction is added to the contents of the X register (carry discarded). This gives the address of the low byte of the effective address. The next location holds the high byte of the effective address.
8. Indirect Indexed (IND, Y). The second byte of the instruction holds an address in page zero; this and the next byte hold a 16-bit address which is added to the contents of the Y register to give the effective address.
9. Implied. Address implied in op. code.
10. Relative to Program Counter.

## Arithmetic and Logical Operations

| *INSTRUCTION* | *MNEMONIC* | *ADDRESS MODE* | | | | | | | |
|---|---|---|---|---|---|---|---|---|---|
| | | *1* | *2* | *3* | *4* | *5* | *6* | *7* | *8* |
| Add with Carry | ADC | 69 | 6D | 65 | 75 | 7D | 79 | 61 | 71 |
| AND with Acc. | AND | 29 | 2D | 25 | 35 | 3D | 39 | 21 | 31 |
| Arithmetic Shift Left | ASL | | 0E | 06 | 16 | 1E | | | |
| Bit Test Memory with Acc. | BIT | | 2C | 24 | | | | | |
| Compare Memory with Acc. | CMP | C9 | CD | C5 | D5 | DD | D9 | C1 | D1 |
| Compare Memory and X | CPX | E0 | EC | E4 | | | | | |
| Decrement | DEC | | CE | C6 | D6 | DE | | | |
| Compare Memory and Y | CPY | C0 | CC | C4 | | | | | |
| Exclusive-OR Memory and Acc. | EOR | 49 | 4D | 45 | 55 | 5D | 59 | 41 | 51 |
| Increment Memory | INC | | EE | E6 | F6 | FE | | | |
| Jump | JMP | | 4C | | | | | | |
| Jump to Subroutine | JSR | | 20 | | | | | | |
| Load Acc. | LDA | A9 | AD | A5 | B5 | BD | B9 | A1 | B1 |
| Load Index Reg. X | LDX | A2 | AE | A6 | | | BE | | |
| Load Index Reg. Y | LDY | A0 | AC | A4 | B4 | BC | | | |
| Logical Shift Right | LSR | | 4E | 46 | 56 | 5E | | | |
| OR with Acc. | ORA | 09 | 0D | 05 | 15 | 1D | 19 | 01 | 11 |
| Rotate Left with Carry | ROL | | 2E | 26 | 36 | 3E | | | |
| Rotate Right with Carry | ROR | | 6E | 66 | 76 | 7E | | | |
| Subtract with Carry | SBC | E9 | ED | E5 | F5 | FD | F9 | E1 | F1 |
| Store Acc. | STA | | 8D | 85 | 95 | 9D | 99 | 81 | 91 |
| Store Index Reg. X | STX | | 8E | 86 | | | | | |
| Store Index Reg. Y | STY | | 8C | 84 | 94 | | | | |

## Instructions with Implied Addressing

| *INSTRUCTION* | *MNEMONIC* | *OP. CODE* |
|---|---|---|
| Break – Halts Processor | BRK | 00 |
| Clear Carry Flag | CLC | 18 |
| Clear Decimal Mode | CLD | D8 |
| Clear Interrupt Disable Bit | CLI | 58 |
| Clear Overflow Bit | CLV | B8 |
| Decrement Index Reg. X | DEX | CA |
| Decrement Index Reg. Y | DEY | 88 |
| Increment Index Reg. X | INX | E8 |
| Increment Index Reg. Y | INY | C8 |
| No operation | NOP | EA |
| Push Acc. on Stack | PHA | 48 |
| Push Proc. Status on Stack | PHP | 08 |
| Pull from Stack to Acc. | PLA | 68 |
| Pull from Stack to Proc. Status | PLP | 28 |
| Return from Interrupt | RTI | 40 |
| Return from Subroutine | RTS | 60 |
| Set Carry Flag | SEC | 38 |
| Set Decimal Mode | SED | F8 |
| Set Interrupt Disable Bit | SEI | 78 |
| Transfer Acc. to Index Reg. X | TAX | AA |
| Transfer Acc. to Index Reg. Y | TAY | A8 |
| Transfer Stack Pointer to Index X | TSX | BA |
| Transfer Index X to Acc. | TXA | 8A |
| Transfer Index X to Stack Pointer | TXS | 9A |
| Transfer Index Y to Acc. | TYA | 98 |

## Branch Instructions with Relative Addressing

| *INSTRUCTION* | *MNEMONIC* | *OP. CODE* |
|---|---|---|
| Branch if Carry Clear | BCC | 90 |
| Branch if Carry Set | BCS | B0 |
| Branch if Result Zero | BEQ | F0 |
| Branch if Minus | BMI | 30 |
| Branch if Not Zero | BNE | D0 |
| Branch if Plus | BPL | 10 |
| Branch if Overflow Clear | BVC | 50 |
| Branch if Overflow Set | BVS | 70 |

# Appendix 4: 68000 Instruction Set

| MNEMONIC | | ACTION | OPERAND SIZE |
|---|---|---|---|
| ABCD | S,D | Add Binary Coded Decimal and X bit | B |
| ADD | S,D | Add Binary Data | B,W,L |
| ADDA | S,D | Add Address | W,L |
| ADDI | #X,D | Add Immediate Data | B,W,L |
| ADDQ | #X,D | Add Data Quick | B,W,L |
| ADDX | S,D | Add Data and X bit | B,W,L |
| AND | S,D | Logical AND Operation | B,W,L |
| ANDI | #X,D | Logical AND with Immediate Operand | B,W,L |
| ANDI | #X,CCR | Logical AND with Immediate Operand to CCR | B |
| ANDI | #X,SR | Logical AND with Immediate Operand to SR (P) | B |
| ASL | #X,D | Arithmetic Shift Left | B,W,L |
| ASR | #X,D | Arithmetic Shift Right | B,W,L |
| BCC | label | Branch if Carry Clear | B,W |
| BCS | label | Branch if Carry Set | B,W |
| BEQ | label | Branch if Equal | B,W |
| BGE | label | Branch if Greater than or Equal | B,W |
| BGT | label | Branch if Greater than | B,W |
| BHI | label | Branch if High | B,W |
| BLE | label | Branch if Less than or Equal | B,W |
| BLS | label | Branch if Less than or Same | B,W |
| BLT | label | Branch if Less than | B,W |
| BMI | label | Branch if Minus | B,W |
| BNE | label | Branch if not Equal | B,W |
| BPL | label | Branch if Plus | B,W |
| BVC | label | Branch if Overflow Clear | B,W |
| BVS | label | Branch if Overflow Set | B,W |
| BRA | label | Branch Always | B,W |
| BCHG | bit,D | Test a Bit and Change | B,L |
| BCLR | bit,D | Test a Bit and Clear | B,L |
| BSET | bit,D | Test a Bit and Set | B,L |
| BSR | label | Branch to Subroutine | B,W |
| BTST | bit,D | Test a Bit | B,L |

| | | | |
|---|---|---|---|
| CHK | S,Dn | Check Register against Bounds | W |
| CLR | D | Clear an Operand | B,W,L |
| CMP | S,Dn | Compare Operands | B,W,L |
| CMPA | S,An | Compare Addresses | W,L |
| CMPI | #X,D | Compare Operand with Immediate Data | B,W,L |
| CMPM | S,D | Compare Operands held in Memory | B,W,L |
| DBcc | Dn, label | Test Condition, Decrement and Branch | W |
| | | cc denotes condition as in Branch Instructions | |
| DIVS | S,Dn | Divide Signed Numbers | W |
| DIVU | S,Dn | Divide Unsigned Numbers | W |
| EOR | Dn,D | Exclusive OR Operation | B,W,L |
| EORI | #X,D | Exclusive OR with Immediate Operand | B,W,L |
| EORI | #X,CCR | Exclusive OR Immediate with CC Register | B |
| EORI | #X,SR | Exclusive OR Immediate with Status Register | W |
| EXG | Rx, Ry | Exchange Registers | L |
| EXT | Dn | Extend Sign | L |
| JMP | label | Jump | – |
| JSR | label | Jump to Subroutine | – |
| LEA | D,An | Load Effective Address | L |
| LSL | #X,Dn | Logical Shift Left | B,W,L |
| LSR | #X,Dn | Logical Shift Right | B,W,L |
| MOVE | S,D | Move Data from Source to Destination | B,W,L |
| MOVE | CCR,D | Move from CC Register | W |
| MOVE | S,CCR | Move to CC Register | W |
| MOVE | SR,D | Move from Status Register | W |
| MOVE | S,SR | Move to Status Register | W |
| MOVEA | S,An | Move Address | W,L |
| MOVEM | Regs, D | Move Multiple Registers to Memory | W,L |
| MOVEM | S, Regs | Move Multiple Registers from Memory | W,L |
| MOVEP | S,D | Move Peripheral Data | W,L |
| MOVEQ | #X,Dn | Move Quick – Immediate Data to Data Register | L |
| MULS | S,D | Multiply Signed Numbers | W |
| MULU | S,D | Multiply Unsigned Numbers | W |
| NBCD | D | Negate Decimal with Extend | B |
| NEG | D | Negate Operand | B,W,L |
| NEGX | D | Negate with Extend | B,W,L |
| NOP | | No Operation | – |
| NOT | D | Logical Complement | B,W,L |
| OR | S,D | Logical Inclusive OR | B,W,L |
| ORI | #X,D | Logical Inclusive OR with Immediate Operand | B,W,L |
| ORI | #X,CCR | Logical Inclusive OR Immediate with CCR | B |
| ORI | #X,SR | Logical Inclusive OR Immediate with SR | W |
| PEA | S | Push Effective Address onto Stack | L |

| | | | |
|---|---|---|---|
| ROL | #X,Dn | Rotate Left without Extend | B,W,L |
| ROR | #X,Dn | Rotate Right without Extend | B,W,L |
| ROXL | #X,Dn | Rotate Left with Extend | B,W,L |
| ROXR | #X,Dn | Rotate Right with Extend | B,W,L |
| RTE | | Return from Exception | — |
| RTR | | Return and Restore Condition Codes | — |
| RTS | | Return from Subroutine | — |
| SBCD | S,D | Subtract Decimal with Extend | B |
| Scc | D | Set Byte if Condition is True, Else Clear | B |
| | | cc denotes condition as in Branch Instructions | |
| SUB | S, D | Subtract Binary | B,W,L |
| SUBA | S,An | Subtract Addresses | W,L |
| SUBI | #X,D | Subtract Immediate | B,W,L |
| SUBQ | #X,D | Subtract Quick, Immediate | B,W,L |
| SUBX | S,D | Subtract Binary with Extend | B,W,L |
| SWAP | Dn | Swap Register Halves | W |
| TAS | D | Test and Set Byte | B |
| TRAP | #X | Start Exception Processing, X gives vector | — |
| TRAPV | | Trap ₁₁ Overflow Bit is Set | — |
| TST | D | Test Operand | B,W,L |

*SYMBOLS*

D   Destination Operand.
S   Source Operand.
An  Address Register.
Dn  Data Register.
#X  Immediate Data.
cc  Condition Mnemonics for Conditional Branches.

# Appendix 5: The ASCII Code

The American Standard Code for Information Interchange is widely used for communicating between computers and terminals. It has been given international recognition as ISO-7 code. This specifies only 7 bits, but an 8-bit byte is generally allocated to transmit each character; the 8th bit can be used to produce odd or even parity, or it can be set always to a one or a zero. The first 20 (hex) codes are non-printing codes which perform a control function.

| Hex Code | Character | Meaning |
|---|---|---|
| 00 | NUL | Null |
| 01 | SOH | Start of header |
| 02 | STX | Start of text |
| 03 | ETX | End of text |
| 04 | EOT | End of transmission |
| 05 | ENQ | Enquiry |
| 06 | ACK | Acknowledge |
| 07 | BEL | Bell |
| 08 | BS | Backspace |
| 09 | HT | Horizontal tabulation |
| 0A | LF | Line feed |
| 0B | VT | Vertical tabulation |
| 0C | FF | Form feed |
| 0D | CR | Carriage return |
| 0E | SO | Shift out |
| 0F | SI | Shift in |
| 10 | DLE | Data link escape |
| 11 | DC1 | |
| 12 | DC2 | Device control |
| 13 | DC3 | |
| 14 | DC4 | |
| 15 | NAK | Negative acknowledge |
| 16 | SYN | Synchronous idle |
| 17 | ETB | End of transmission block |
| 18 | CAN | Cancel |
| 19 | EM | End of medium |
| 1A | SUB | Substitute character |

| 1B | ESC | Escape |
|---|---|---|
| 1C | FS | File separator |
| 1D | GS | Group separator |
| 1E | RS | Record separator |
| 1F | US | Unit separator |
| 20 | space | — |
| 21 | ! | — |
| 22 | " | — |
| 23 | # or £ | — |
| 24 | $ | — |
| 25 | % | — |
| 26 | & | — |
| 27 | ' | — |
| 28 | ( | — |
| 29 | ) | — |
| 2A | * | — |
| 2B | + | — |
| 2C | , | — |
| 2D | - | — |
| 2E | . | — |
| 2F | / | — |
| 30 | 0 | — |
| 31 | 1 | — |
| 32 | 2 | — |
| 33 | 3 | — |
| 34 | 4 | — |
| 35 | 5 | — |
| 36 | 6 | — |
| 37 | 7 | — |
| 38 | 8 | — |
| 39 | 9 | — |
| 3A | : | — |
| 3B | ; | — |
| 3C | < | — |
| 3D | = | — |
| 3E | > | — |
| 3F | ? | — |
| 40 | @ | — |
| 41 | A | — |
| 42 | B | — |
| 43 | C | — |
| 44 | D | — |
| 45 | E | — |
| 46 | F | — |

| 47 | G | — |
|----|---|---|
| 48 | H | — |
| 49 | I | — |
| 4A | J | — |
| 4B | K | — |
| 4C | L | — |
| 4D | M | — |
| 4E | N | — |
| 4F | O | — |
| 50 | P | — |
| 51 | Q | — |
| 52 | R | — |
| 53 | S | — |
| 54 | T | — |
| 55 | U | — |
| 56 | V | — |
| 57 | W | — |
| 58 | X | — |
| 59 | Y | — |
| 5A | Z | — |
| 5B | [ | — |
| 5C | \ | — |
| 5D | ] | — |
| 5E | ^ | — |
| 5F | _ | — |
| 60 | ` | — |
| 61 | a | — |
| 62 | b | — |
| 63 | c | — |
| 64 | d | — |
| 65 | e | — |
| 66 | f | — |
| 67 | g | — |
| 68 | h | — |
| 69 | i | — |
| 6A | j | — |
| 6B | k | — |
| 6C | l | — |
| 6D | m | — |
| 6E | n | — |
| 6F | o | — |
| 70 | p | — |
| 71 | q | — |
| 72 | r | — |

| | | |
|---|---|---|
| 73 | s | – |
| 74 | t | – |
| 75 | u | – |
| 76 | v | – |
| 77 | w | – |
| 78 | x | – |
| 79 | y | – |
| 7A | z | – |
| 7B | { | – |
| 7C | \| | – |
| 7D | } | – |
| 7E | ~ | – |
| 7F | DEL | (Delete) |

# Bibliography

Andrews, M., *Programming Microprocessor Interfaces for Control and Instrumentation*, Prentice-Hall International, Hemel Hempstead, 1982

Bacon, J., *The Motorola MC68000*, Prentice-Hall International, Hemel Hempstead, 1986

Barrow, D., *68000 Machine Code Programming*, Collins, London, 1985

Carr, J., *6502 User's Manual*, Prentice-Hall International, Hemel Hempstead, 1984

Coats, R.B., *Software Engineering for Small Computers*, Edward Arnold, London, 1982

Depledge, P. (Ed.), *Software Engineering for Microprocessor Systems*, Peter Peregrinus, London, 1984

Elfring, G.C., *Microcomputer Assembly Language Programming*, Van-Nostrand-Reinhold, New York, 1984

Erskine, R., *Assembly Language for the 8086 and 8088*, Pitman, London, 1985

Foster, C.C., *Programming a Microcomputer: the 6502*, Addison-Wesley, Reading, Massachusetts, 1978

Hutty, R., *Z80 Assembly Language Programming for Students*, Macmillan, London, 1981

James, M., *The 6809 Companion*, Bernard Babani, London, 1982

Jaulent, P., *The 68000 Hardware and Software*, Macmillan, London, 1985

Leventhal, L.H., *6800 Assembly Language Programming*, Adam Osborne and Associates, Berkeley, California, 1978

Leventhal, L.H., *6502 Assembly Language Programming*, 2nd edn, Osborne/McGraw-Hill, Berkeley, California, 1988

Leventhal, L.H., Osborne, A. and Collins, C., *Z8000 Assembly Language Programming*, Osborne/McGraw-Hill, Berkeley, California, 1980

Lister, P.F. (Ed.), *Single Chip Microcomputers*, Granada, London, 1984

Miller, A.R., *8080/Z80 Assembly Language: Techniques for Improved Programming*, Wiley, Chichester, 1981

Morse, S.P., *The 8086/8088 Primer*, 2nd edn, Hayden, New Jersey, 1982

Motorola Inc., *The MC68000 Data Manual*, Motorola Inc., Austin, Texas, 1983

Osborne, A. and Kane, G., *16 Bit Microprocessor Handbook*, Osborne/McGraw-Hill, Berkeley, California, 1981

Penfold, R.A. and Penfold, J.W., *An Introduction to 6502 Machine Code*, Bernard Babini, London, 1984

Penfold, R.A. and Penfold, J.W., *An Introduction to Z80 Machine Code*, Bernard Babani, London, 1984

Raven, T., *16 Bit Microprocessor Handbook*, Newnes, Twickenham, 1986

Stephenson, A.P., *6502 Machine Code for Beginners*, Butterworth, Sevenoaks, Kent, 1983

Trio, J.M., *8086/8088 Architecture and Programming*, Macmillan, London, 1985

Walker, B.S., *Understanding Microprocessors*, Macmillan, London, 1981

Whitworth, I.R., *16 Bit Microprocessors*, Collins, London, 1985

Yeung, S.J., *8086/8088 Assembly Language Programming*, Wiley, Chichester, 1984

Zilog Inc., *Z80 Technical Manual*, Zilog Inc., Cupertino, California, 1977

Zilog Inc., *Z8000 CPU User's Reference Manual*, Prentice-Hall International, Hemel Hempstead, 1982

# *Glossary*

| | |
|---|---|
| **Accumulator** | A register used to hold the result of an arithmetic or logic operation. |
| **Address** | A number which identifies a particular place or location in the store capable of holding 1 byte of information. |
| **ALU** | Arithmetic and Logic Unit, the central calculating unit of the microprocessor. |
| **Assembler** | A program which converts assembly language into binary code which the microprocessor can execute. |
| **Assembly language** | A method of writing instructions which uses mnemonic terms such as ADD instead of binary numbers, and names instead of addresses. |
| **BASIC** | A high level language available on most microprocessors. |
| **Binary number** | A number coded in base 2, using the digits 1 and 0. |
| **Bit** | Short for binary digit. |
| **Bus** | A set of lines which connect parts of a microcomputer, all having the same function — for example, data bus, address bus. |
| **Byte** | 8 bits which are handled as one item. |
| **Clock** | A constant-frequency train of pulses used to synchronise the actions of the various parts of a computer. |
| **CPU** | Central Processing Unit of a computer system. |
| **Data** | An item of information being processed. |
| **Editor** | A program which allows a user to create and alter a file. |
| **Execute** | To carry out an instruction. |
| **Fetch** | To extract the next instruction from the program store. |
| **File** | A set of data which can be stored as a single unit. |
| **Flag** | A single bit store used to indicate some event or condition. |
| **Format** | The way in which data is arranged. |
| **Hexadecimal** | Coded in base 16. |
| **Index register** | A register whose contents are used to calculate the address of an operand. |
| **Instruction** | A binary code which determines a single processor operation. |
| **Interrupt** | An event which causes the microprocessor to transfer its attention from the current program to another program which serves the device responsible for the event. |

| | |
|---|---|
| **Location** | A storage register having a unique address. |
| **Machine code** | Instructions in binary code which the microprocessor can execute directly. |
| **Macro** | A set of assembly language instructions which can be inserted into a program by quoting the macro name. |
| **Memory** | The storage devices which hold the program and data. |
| **Microprocessor** | An integrated circuit which performs the central processing function of a complete system. |
| **Operand** | A data item which an instruction operates on. |
| **Operation code** | (Op. code) The part of an instruction which determines the operation to be performed. |
| **Peripheral** | An external device connected to the microprocessor. |
| **Processor** | A unit which fetches and executes instructions. |
| **Program** | A sequence of statements or instructions. |
| **Program counter** | A processor register which holds the address of the next instruction to be executed. |
| **RAM** | Random Access Memory. Memory in which any item can be accessed equally quickly. By convention, can be both read from and written to. |
| **Register** | A storage place for data (usually one word); if in the processor it provides fast access. |
| **ROM** | Read Only Memory. |
| **Run** | To execute a program. |
| **Serial** | Following one another in time. |
| **Source program** | A program in its original form. |
| **Status register** | A register which holds data on the state or condition of a system. |
| **VDU** | Visual Display Unit. A terminal containing a keyboard and a television type of display. |
| **Word** | A group of bits which are processed and transferred as a single entity. |

# *Index*